How to Read
Schematic Diagrams

by

DONALD E. HERRINGTON

HOWARD W. SAMS & CO., INC.
THE BOBBS-MERRILL CO., INC.
INDIANAPOLIS · KANSAS CITY · NEW YORK

SECOND EDITION

SECOND PRINTING — 1968

Library of Congress Catalog Card Number: 67-26998

Preface

Who would think of starting on a cross-country trip without first consulting a road map and plotting the route? Schematic diagrams and road maps have a lot in common—both show the "highways" from one point to another, and both use symbols to designate the various "landmarks." Yet, many students try to embark on a much more important trip—a career in electronics—without first learning how to properly read the "road maps" of the trade.

A simple key to the symbols, such as that included on most maps, is not sufficient for electronic schematics. The highways, cities, rivers, etc., on the road map are familiar to everyone—you immediately have a picture of what is being represented. The components which make up electronic circuits, however, are not as familiar. Before you can look at an electronic symbol and get a mental picture of its effect on the circuit, you must first know something about the component it represents. This book was written to help you gain this needed understanding. The comments and letters received have indicated this goal has been accomplished. This second edition contains many added symbols and expanded explanations to keep in step with the latest developments.

Only the theory considered necessary for this knowledge is given. Once the purpose of a component is understood, you will see that its symbol is just as representative as the line across a map is of a highway.

The later chapters in this book show how these components are combined to form circuits. Then, step by step, you follow signals through a schematic diagram of a radio receiver. The function of each stage and the meaning of the information on the schematic is explained.

This book has been written with the beginner or hobbyist in mind, but it can also serve as an invaluable reference for the technician.

DONALD E. HERRINGTON

To Thelma, Linda, and Bryan . . .
. . . for their assistance and encouragement.

Contents

CHAPTER 1

Types of Electronic Diagrams

Many types of diagrams are needed to completely describe the operation and construction of electronic equipment. The most widely used, of course, is the *schematic* diagram—the subject of this book. A schematic is usually all that is required for analyzing, explaining, and servicing most circuits. But as we shall see, it cannot convey all the information about a piece of equipment; other types of diagrams are needed as well.

In this chapter we will discuss each of the different types, pointing out their particular advantages and disadvantages.

SCHEMATIC DIAGRAMS

The first questions the layman or student may ask when confronted by a schematic are "Why use all of these symbols? Couldn't the same information be given without resorting to the use of sign language? Is this just a conspiracy among people in electronics to keep us from learning the art?" The answer to the last two questions, as you will see, is no.

Why Schematics and Symbols?

Symbols are used in electronic diagrams because experience has shown us they are the quickest and easiest way to convey the needed information. Simple symbols are a form of electronic shorthand. With them a circuit can be sketched in a short time; and because the symbols are standard, they can be easily interpreted by other persons.

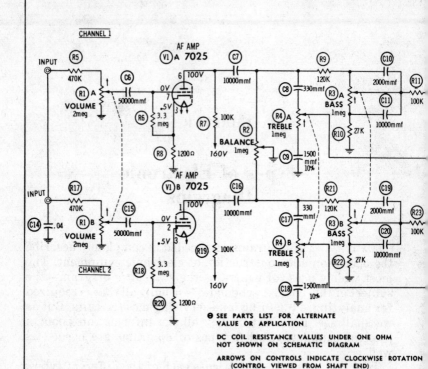

CHANNEL 1

AF AMP
V1 A 7025

INPUT R5 470K R1 A VOLUME 2meg C6 50000mmf R6 R8 1200Ω

6 100V 0V 7 .5V 3 3.3 meg

C7 10000mmf R7 100K R2 BALANCE 1meg 160V

C9 1500 mmf 10%

R9 120K C8 330mmf R4 A TREBLE 1meg R3 A BASS 1meg R10 27K C10 2000mmf C11 10000mmf R11 100K

AF AMP
V1 B 7025

INPUT C14 .04 R17 470K R1 B VOLUME 2meg C15 50000mmf R18 R20 1200Ω

CHANNEL 2

1 100V 0V 2 .5V 3 3.3 meg

C16 10000mmf R19 100K 160V

C18 1500mmf 10%

R21 120K 330 mmf C17 R4 B TREBLE 1meg R3 B BASS 1meg R22 27K C19 2000mmf C20 10000mmf R23 100K

⊖ SEE PARTS LIST FOR ALTERNATE
VALUE OR APPLICATION

DC COIL RESISTANCE VALUES UNDER ONE OHM
NOT SHOWN ON SCHEMATIC DIAGRAM

ARROWS ON CONTROLS INDICATE CLOCKWISE ROTATION
(CONTROL VIEWED FROM SHAFT END)

RESISTANCE READINGS

ITEM	TUBE	Pin 1	Pin 2	Pin 3	Pin 4	Pin 5	Pin 6	Pin 7	Pin 8	Pin 9
V1	7025 12AX7	† 118K	3.3meg	1200Ω	10Ω	0Ω	† 118K	3.3meg	1200Ω	5Ω
V2	12AX7	† 118K	130K	1800Ω	20Ω	10Ω	† 118K	130K	1800Ω	15Ω
V3	50L6GT	NC	105Ω	† 630Ω	† 24K	470K	TP	60Ω	95Ω	
V4	50L6GT	TP	60Ω	† 690Ω	† 24K	470K	TP	20Ω	95Ω	

† MEASURED FROM OUTPUT OF M2.   NC NO CONNECTION   TP TIE POINT

1. DC voltage measurements taken with vacuum tube voltmeter;
   AC voltages measured with 1000 ohm per volt voltmeter.
2. Socket connections are shown as bottom views.
3. Measured values are from socket pin to common ground.
4. Line voltage maintained at 117 volts for voltage readings.
5. Nominal tolerance of component values makes possible a
   variation of ± 15% in voltage and resistance readings.
6. All controls at minimum, proper output load connected.

Fig. 1-1. Schematic of a typical

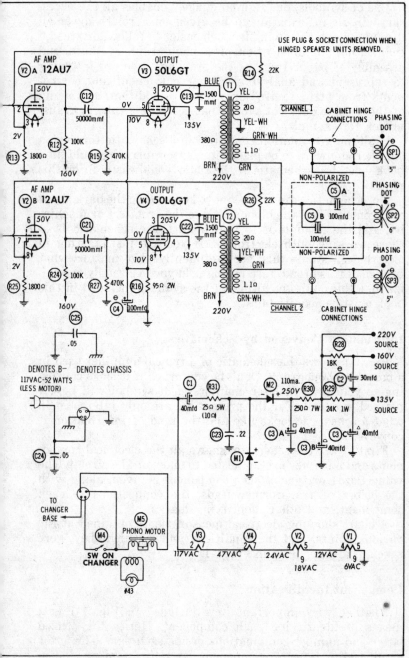

stereo phono amplifier.

Use of symbols, or "sign language," enables all the necessary circuit information to be given on a relatively small drawing. Such a drawing is much easier to follow, or "read," than either an illustration or a photograph of the actual assembly of parts. Imagine the problems involved in trying to represent and analyze electronic equipment and components from "true-to-life" drawings! In addition, a drawing of the outside does not show what is inside a tube or transmitter, for example.

If all the information contained in a schematic for even a simple radio were to be placed in written form, it would fill a book—yet, the schematic of the radio would easily fit on this page!

No, schematics are not meant to keep you in the dark about electronics. What the blueprint is to the architect or machinist, and the formula is to the chemist, the schematic is to those working with electronics. If you are just starting in electronics, study this book diligently. No matter what branch of this broad, fascinating field you eventually specialize in, a thorough knowledge of the symbols included in this book must be acquired first.

Information Conveyed by Schematics

Fig. 1-1 shows the schematic of a typical amplifier used in a portable phonograph. Don't be concerned if it looks confusing to you now. In later chapters each symbol will be explained in detail. For the present we are only interested in what a schematic looks like and the kind of information it conveys.

First of all, the schematic shows all the electrical components and how they are connected to make up the circuit. The value (size) or type of each component is given, along with the colors of transformer leads, the connections to each component, and other identifying marks.

A chart showing electrical measurements obtained at the various points, and the conditions under which they were taken, is also included in Fig. 1-1.

Component Identification

Another very important item included in Fig. 1-1 is a means of identifying each component. Notice the circled letter-and-number combinations beside each part. The letter signifies the type of component, and the number distinguishes it from all others of the same type. For instance, instead of saying "the 5,000-mmf capacitor connected between the volume control and pin 7 of the 7025 tube," we can merely say "C6."

Other portions of the literature concerning a particular piece of equipment will also use these same letter-and-number designations. For instance, C6 may appear in a parts list which gives the part numbers and specifications for each component, and also on a photo or drawing which shows its location. Thus, by using the same designation in all places to identify a component, there is less chance for an error to be made.

Unfortunately, all manufacturers do not designate a given component by the same code letters (or "call-outs" as they are sometimes called). However, they are fairly standard and usually only a few items will be different. The code letters used by Howard W. Sams & Co., Inc., appear in Table 1-1. In later chapters the code letters used by others will be given where they differ from the code letters that are used by Howard W. Sams & Co., Inc.

Table 1-1. Code Letter Designation Used by
Howard W. Sams & Co., Inc.

CODE LETTER	
C	Capacitors (all types), spark plates
F	Fuses, circuit breakers
K	Relays
L	Coils, chokes, RF and IF transformers
M	Batteries, crystals, microphones, phono pick-ups, magnetic heads, meters, and other miscellaneous components
PC	Component combinations
Q	Transistors (all types)
R	Resistors; (all types including varistors, thermistors, LDR's, etc.)
S	Switches
SP	Speakers
T	Iron-core transformers; television sweep transformers
V	Tubes
X	Semiconductor diodes, power rectifiers, varactors, scr's, zener diodes, etc.

Symbol Variation

Like the code letters, the symbols used by different companies also differ. The symbols for each component will be discussed in the following chapters, and where differences exist, the various ways of depicting a given item will be shown.

Organizations such as the Institute of Electrical and Electronic Engineers (IEEE) have adopted standard symbols which they hope the industry will use. Likewise, there are standards adopted by the American Standards Association and the military services, which fortunately, are identical. Recently, the Electronic Industries Association (EIA) has been instrumental in coordinating the efforts of various groups aimed at standardization of symbols.

The symbols used throughout the world are fairly standard. Once the symbols given in this book are mastered, you should have no problem understanding a schematic from anywhere—except of course, foreign terms will be used on it. The differences between two U.S. schematics may be greater than between a U.S. and a foreign schematic.

Fortunately, the differences in the symbol used by various companies to depict a component are not so great as in previous years. Differences still exist, however, so in the later chapters of this book, the symbols used by various companies will be shown. In general, the weight of a line or minor differences do not change the meaning of a symbol. In fact, the symbol can be completely reversed; that is, two symbols can be the mirror image of each other and still have the same meaning.

Most of the differences in the symbols chosen stem from differences in the type of drafting and the method of laying out the circuit; they have no effect on the meaning. Schematics may be hand sketched, drawn with ink and a symbol guide, produced using preprinted symbols, or even prepared by a machine having a keyboard similar to that of a typesetting machine. Therefore, minor differences are inevitable.

BLOCK DIAGRAMS

The block diagram (Fig. 1-2) is also often used in electronics. Even though it does not provide as much information as the schematic, it nevertheless is very useful because it is easier to interpret for certain limited purposes.

The principal use of the block diagram is to show the overall operation of the circuit—in other words, the inter-relationships of the various stages. Additional blocks will often be included to provide other information. The diagram in Fig. 1-2 is "read" by starting with the block farthest to the left, labeled "Stereo Phono Cartridge," then following the

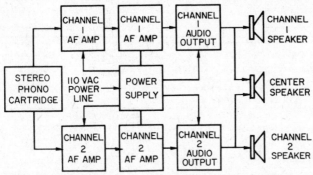

Fig. 1-2. Block diagram of the phono amplifier in Fig. 1-1.

arrows through the two AF amplifiers, the audio-output tube, and ending at the speakers. Since this is a stereo amplifier, two arrows extend from the phono-cartridge block—one leading to the top row of blocks and the other to the bottom row. These two rows represent the amplifiers for the two channels of the stereo system. Notice that this unit has, in addition to a speaker for each individual channel, a center speaker to which the signals from both channels are fed. The block in the center, labeled "Power Supply," furnishes all the other blocks with the necessary power.

In summary, a block diagram shows the path of the signal through the circuit, and the function of each stage. It does not furnish any information about the type of connections or components; hence, it has only limited use. But for only a brief look at the over-all operation and functions of a unit, the block diagram is the simplest and easiest to follow.

CHASSIS-LAYOUT DIAGRAMS

A third type of diagram appears in Fig. 1-3. Often called a *tube placement chart*, it shows the physical locations of the major components. (Note: this is the same stereo phono-graph shown in Figs. 1-1 and 1-2.) A placement chart is extremely useful for more complicated pieces of equipment such as television receivers. As more and more tubes and other components are added, the task of determining just which tube or transistor fulfills a given function becomes more difficult. With a diagram like the one in Fig. 1-3, locating a certain tube is greatly simplified. The dashed lines for the controls indicate they are located under the chassis.

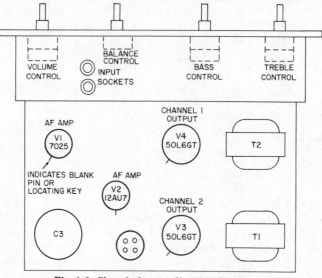

Fig. 1-3. Chassis-layout diagram for the
phono amplifier in Fig. 1-1.

Notice the short lines intersecting the circles representing tubes. All tubes have some method of orientation in the socket—either a blank space or a locating key on the base. This short line indicates either the position of the blank space or the direction in which the locating key points on the socket. By noting the position of this line on the diagram, and by turning the tube so that its blank space or locating key is pointed in this direction, its insertion into the socket is made much easier—especially if the tube socket is hard to reach.

PHOTOS AND PICTORIAL DIAGRAMS

The schematic diagram has one important limitation—it does not show the actual physical location of the individual components. Even though it shows all electrical connections

14

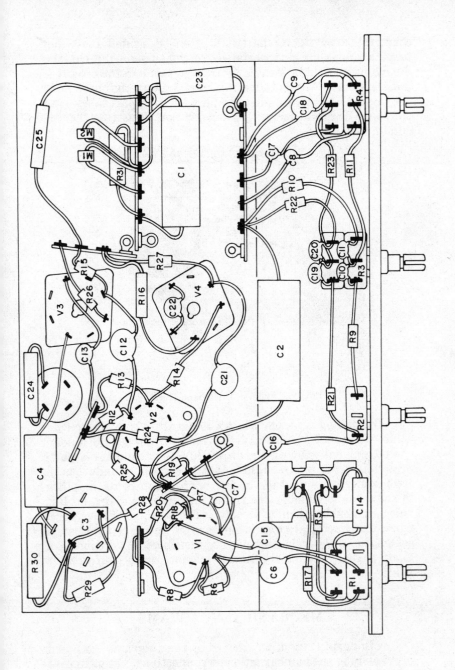

Fig. 1-4. Pictorial diagram of underside of a phono-amplifier chassis.

15

correctly, a particular part will often be located some distance away from its associated components on the chassis. Such a part could be located by tracing through the circuit—but the easiest way is to use a pictorial diagram like the one shown in Fig. 1-4, or a photograph with each part labeled, as shown in Fig. 1-5. (Figs. 1-4 and 1-5 both illustrate the circuit in Fig. 1-1.)

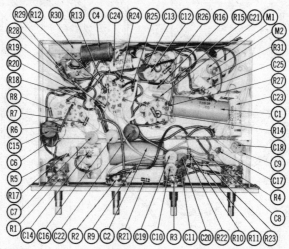

Fig. 1-5. Photo of underside of phono-amplifier chassis.

In the photograph, parts located beneath other components cannot be seen. In such a case the line pointing out the hidden component will stop on the object hiding it, and the arrowhead will be omitted to signify that it is the part underneath.

The only disadvantage of the photograph is its inability to show connections as clearly as the pictorial diagram. But neither can show them as clearly as the schematic. Therefore, when the electrical connections are of primary interest, a schematic is used; but when only the physical location of a given part is desired, a pictorial or photograph is of greater value.

MECHANICAL DIAGRAMS

One important function ignored by the diagrams discussed previously is mechanical action or connections. Let us look at a few of the more common types of diagrams used for this purpose.

Dial-Cord Stringing

Replacing a dial cord on a receiver can be a most difficult and, in some instances, an impossible task without proper instruction. Fig. 1-6 shows a diagram prepared to provide the necessary information to make the job comparatively easy.

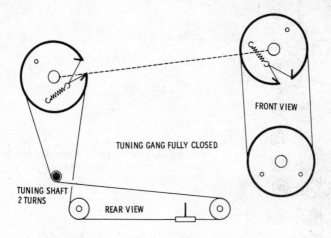

FRONT VIEW

TUNING GANG FULLY CLOSED

TUNING SHAFT
2 TURNS

REAR VIEW

Fig. 1-6. A dial-cord stringing diagram.

Without such help, hours might be spent trying to determine the correct method, especially for more complicated arrangements.

"Exploded" Views

For certain pieces of electrical and electronic equipment the operation of which is largely mechanical (such as record changers and tape recorders), the interrelationship between parts can best be shown on a diagram known as an "exploded" view. Fig. 1-7 shows such a diagram of the 45-rpm spindle used with the amplifier previously discussed. Note that each part is "exploded" from its normal position. The relationship of each part with respect to all the others is maintained, however, and the dashed lines point to their correct position in the assembly. Each part is identified by a circled number. By referring to this number in the parts list, the name and description of the item, as well as the manufacturer's part number (if a replacement must be ordered), can be determined.

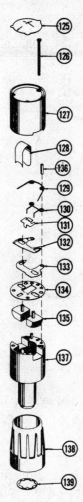

Fig. 1-7. Exploded view of the 45-rpm spindle for a record changer.

REVIEW OF FUNDAMENTALS

While this book is not intended as a text on basic electronic theory, a brief review of fundamental principles may be of value, especially in understanding some of the terms used in the chapters to follow.

Electron Theory

All matter is composed of atoms, made up of a nucleus surrounded by small particles rotating in orbits. These particles, called *electrons*, possess a unit negative charge which is matched in the core of the atom by an equal but opposite positive charge. One of the fundamental laws of nature is that unlike charges attract (like charges repel). Therefore, the electron is attracted to the nucleus, and only the centrifugal force present due to its orbital speed prevents the electron from joining the nucleus.

This attraction between the core of the atom and the orbiting electron is so great that to separate them requires a certain force. Electrons that have been freed will move away from any negative source and toward a positive source. This movement is known as an *electron flow*, or more commonly, an *electric current*, the basic unit of measurement of which is the *ampere*. The force causing this movement is known as a *potential*, or *voltage*, the *volt* being the basic measurement unit.

The atoms in some materials do not hold to their electrons so tightly as do the atoms in others. Such materials are said to be good *conductors*. If the electrons are more tightly held, then the material does not readily permit current flow and is said to be a good *insulator*.

Direct and Alternating Current

The voltage applied to a circuit to cause electron flow can be of many different forms. The simplest is that obtained from a battery. Here, the battery will present to the circuit a

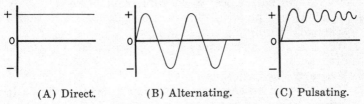

(A) Direct.   (B) Alternating.   (C) Pulsating.

Fig. 1-8. Current waveforms.

constant voltage, negative at one point and positive at the other. The electrons will therefore move from the negative to the positive potential; the quantity is determined by the *amount* of voltage applied and by the degree of opposition offered by the atoms in freeing the electrons. This type of flow, which is constant in quantity, is called *direct current* (DC) since the movement is in only one direction. Fig. 1-8A shows the waveform of such a current. In this graph the distance between the line representing the voltage and the

19

line at the center representing zero voltage signifies the amount of voltage. The fact that this is a straight line shows that it is a constant, DC voltage.

If the applied voltage is caused to change periodically, from a varying positive to a varying negative potential, then the flow is known as *alternating current* (AC), shown graphically in Fig. 1-8B. The most common example is the familiar AC power found in most of today's homes. Here, the voltage reverses itself sixty times each second, causing current to flow first in one direction and then in the other.

There is another type of current, called *pulsating direct current*, often encountered in electronics. It occurs when the voltage varies in value but does not reverse itself. Examination of Fig. 1-8C will reveal that pulsating DC is actually a composite of an AC and a DC waveform, with the AC riding "piggyback" on the DC.

Although an attempt has been made to present the material in this book as clearly as possible, some of the terms may not be familiar to the reader. It is suggested that a basic electronics text be consulted in such instances.

QUESTIONS

1. What is a schematic?
2. How are the individual components on a schematic identified?
3. What information does a block diagram convey?
4. What does a pictorial diagram or picture show that a schematic cannot?
5. What are the advantages of a picture over a pictorial diagram?
6. Why are schematics used?
7. How are record-changer mechanisms usually shown in service literature?
8. What does a chassis-layout diagram show?
9. Name two types of mechanical diagrams.
10. What is the most popular type of electronic diagram?

CHAPTER 2

Resistors

The resistor is probably the most common of all electronic components. Every radio, television, or other piece of electronic equipment will contain several such units.

WHAT IS A RESISTOR?

In electronic circuits, resistors perform exactly the function their name implies—they *resist,* or oppose, the flow of electrons. In other words, a resistor might be said to introduce *electrical friction.* Every electrical component contains a certain amount of resistance, even a piece of ordinary wire. But to obtain the amount of resistance provided by just one resistor might require many feet, or even miles, of wire. By using resistors, however, practically any amount of resistance can be contained in a small, compact unit.

Resistor Ratings

Two types of ratings, or values, are specified for a resistor. The first is the electrical value—how much resistance it will introduce into the circuit. This value is given in *ohms,* the unit of resistance measurement. Thus, if a resistor has a value of 1,000 ohms it will introduce an electrical opposition of 1,000 units to the flow of electrons in a circuit.

This opposition reduces the amount of current flow in a given circuit. By proper selection of resistor value it is possible to obtain the exact amount of current required. Also, when current flows through a resistor a voltage is developed across it. This means that the voltage at one end of a resistor

21

will be lower than at the other end by an amount proportional to the current flow through it. Mathematically, this is expressed as:

$$E = I \times R$$

where,

    E is the voltage in volts,

    I is the current in amperes,

    R is the resistance in ohms.

Thus, the two most important functions of a resistor are: (1) to limit current flow, and (2) to provide a voltage difference.

The second value given in rating a resistor is the *wattage* —how much current can flow through it without causing damage. The unit of measurement is the *watt*, and in general, the larger the physical size of the resistor the higher its wattage rating will be. Common ratings are 1/4, 1/2, 1, 2, and 5 watts or more. Regardless of this wattage rating, however, the resistance of the unit does not change. Thus, a 1/2-watt resistor could be replaced by a 1-watt or even a 5-watt unit. If, however, a 1-watt resistor was replaced by a 1/2-watt unit, the latter might burn out.

Abbreviations and symbols are often used in designating resistor values. For example, the Greek letter *omega* (Ω) is usually employed in the place of the word "ohm." Thus, instead of writing out *100 ohms,* it is usually written as 100Ω. The letter *K* is used to designate 1,000 and *meg* or *megohm* stands for "one million ohms." The *K* is sometimes followed by the Ω sign—at other times it is understood and hence omitted. Thus *100,000 ohms, 100KΩ,* and *100K* all mean the same. *Watts* is usually indicated by the capital letter *W*. For instance, *1W* signifies a 1-watt unit.

FIXED RESISTORS

The fixed resistor is the simplest type. "Fixed" means the unit is constructed in such a way that its ohmic value cannot be varied. Fig. 2-1 shows some examples of this type, each having a certain value determined by the composition and amount of the material from which it is made.

Many fixed resistors are made of a carbon composition— hence the name *carbon resistor*. Others, especially those for high-wattage applications, use a special high-resistance wire wound on a ceramic or other insulating core. This assembly is then covered with a vitreous-enamel protective coating. A cutaway view of this type is shown in Fig. 2-2.

Another type of resistor developed for certain applications is the *metallized* unit. It is constructed by depositing a thin coating of a resistive material onto a glass rod.

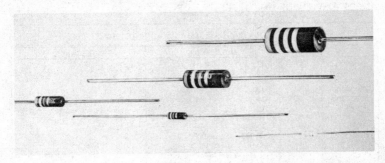

Courtesy Ohmite Manufacturing Co.

Fig. 2-1. An assortment of carbon resistors.

A fixed resistor is usually marked in some way to show the value of the unit. This is most often done by a system of *color coding*. Fig. 2-3 shows the code used for carbon resistors—the most common method shown in Fig. 2-3A and the older methods in Figs. 2-3B, C, and D. In the first method the two bands nearest the end designate the first two figures of the ohmic value, and the third band the number of zeros to be added to arrive at the correct value.

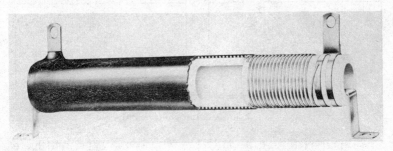

Courtesy Ohmite Manufacturing Co.

Fig. 2-2. Construction of a wirewound resistor.

Thus, a resistor having a yellow, violet, and red band has a value of 4,700 ohms. If a fourth band is present, it will signify how close the resistance is to the indicated value. This is known as the *tolerance*. It is impossible to make each resistor to have the *exact* resistance indicated by its color bands, so certain standard values have been adopted. All resistors which fall within the required percentage of this standard are coded with this value. If no fourth band is present, the resistor is within 20% of the indicated value. A silver band designates 10%, and a gold band, 5% tolerance. Other tolerances are given in Fig. 2-3.

COLOR	DIGIT	MULTIPLIER	TOLERANCE
		RESISTOR CODES (RESISTANCE GIVEN IN OHMS)	
BLACK	0	1	±20%
BROWN	1	10	±1%
RED	2	100	±2%
ORANGE	3	1000	±3%
YELLOW	4	10000	GMV*
GREEN	5	100000	±5% (EIA Alternate)
BLUE	6	1000000	±6%*
VIOLET	7	10000000	±12 1/2%*
GRAY	8	.01 (EIA Alternate)	±30% *
WHITE	9	.1 (EIA Alternate)	±10% (EIA Alternate)
GOLD		.1 (JAN and EIA Preferred)	±5% (JAN and EIA Pref.)
SILVER		.01 (JAN and EIA Preferred)	±10% (JAN and EIA Pref.)
NO COLOR			±20%

*GMV = guaranteed minimum value, or -0 + 100% tolerance.

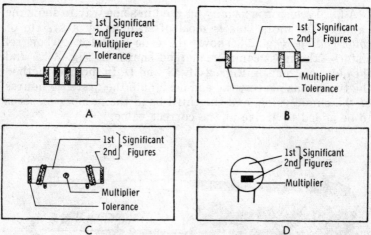

Fig. 2-3. Resistor color codes.

Other resistors, especially the wirewound type, will have the value stamped on the side. The wattage rating will often be included also. Some of the newer resistors are so tiny there is no room for a complete color code. In resistors of this type a special code must be devised; for example, a single red dot might designate a 2,200-ohm resistor.

The schematic symbols for designating fixed resistors are shown in Fig. 2-4. The symbol at A is the most common—those at B and C will seldom be encountered. When the sym-

24

bol at B is used, the value of the resistor will usually be placed inside the box. It is more popular in foreign schematics.

Like the resistance symbol, the code letter used to designate a resistance is also more standardized than most of the others. All American manufacturers designate a fixed resistor by the letter R.

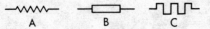

A   B   C

Fig. 2-4. Fixed-resistor symbols.

TAPPED AND ADJUSTABLE RESISTORS

A fixed resistor will sometimes have a tap or connection at some point along the resistance material. Fig. 2-5 shows the symbols used for such a unit. The symbol at A is used almost exclusively and is the same as for a fixed resistor except for the dot and the line connected to the zigzag portion. If there are two taps, another line and dot are added as shown at B.

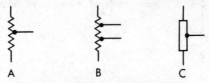

A   B   C

Fig. 2-5. Tapped-resistor symbols.

(The dot is sometimes omitted and the line connected directly to the symbol.) The resistance value of the entire unit, as well as the value at the tapped point, is given for this type of resistor. The symbol at C in Fig. 2-5 is seldom used.

Most tapped resistors are wirewound units with a separate terminal for each tap. In some units the tap is made adjustable by making it in the form of a band around the resistor. The resistance wire is left exposed along one side of the unit and this band makes contact at the desired point. It is then secured by tightening a screw. Fig. 2-6 shows an assortment of wirewound resistors, many having taps. Those at the right in the illustration are adjustable units.

The same symbols shown in Fig. 2-5 are sometimes used to designate these types of adjustable resistors. The dot, however, is usually replaced by an arrowhead, as shown in Fig. 2-7. Like the fixed resistor, R is the code letter always used for both tapped and adjustable resistors.

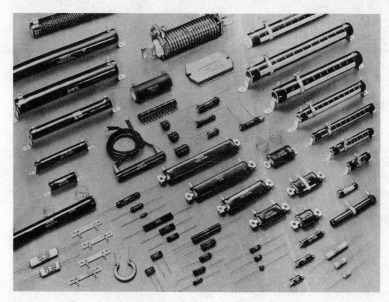

Courtesy Ohmite Manufacturing Co.

Fig. 2-6. A wide variety of wirewound resistors.

Fig. 2-7. Symbols sometimes used for adjustable resistors.

VARIABLE RESISTORS

A resistor which can be continuously varied in value is often needed. The volume control is one of the most common examples. Another use for such a resistor is in lighting circuits to vary the light intensity. For the volume control, the variable resistance is usually called a *potentiometer*, while for the lighting circuit it is usually called a *rheostat*.

Both potentiometers and rheostats are very similar in construction, consisting of a resistance element (usually arranged in a circle) and a sliding contact as shown in Fig. 2-8. As the contact moves along the element the amount of resistance between it and the end of the element changes.

Rheostats are nearly always wirewound, while the element in potentiometers may be either carbon or wire. A potenti-

26

ometer always has three terminals, one at each end of the resistance element and one for the sliding contact. A rheostat, however, may have only two—one at one end of the element and one for the sliding contact.

Courtesy P. R. Mallory & Co., Inc.

Fig. 2-8. An assortment of various size rheostats.

The most common variable-resistor symbols are those labeled A and B in Fig. 2-9. These are alike with the exception that no connection is shown at one end in B. This does not necessarily mean the unit has only two connections. If the third terminal is not used—as is often the case—it is not shown. The symbol at C also designates either a rheostat or potentiometer with only two terminals used. Here, the arrow through the symbol signifies it is adjustable. Five other variations are shown at D, E, F, G, and H. The symbol at E represents a preset adjustment (usually a screwdriver adjustment). Quite often, however, the other symbols are used to represent this type of variable resistor.

The symbol at I signifies a potentiometer that has a tap to provide an additional fixed connection. Some units are made in such a way that the sliding contact will not move beyond a certain point on the element. This always leaves some resistance between the arm and one end of the potentiometer. The symbol for this type is shown at J; the line drawn across the symbol indicates the limit to which the movable contact will travel.

27

The value of a variable resistance may not always be stamped on the unit. The manufacturer's part number is often the only information given. To find the value, refer to the schematic, parts list, or manufacturer's catalog.

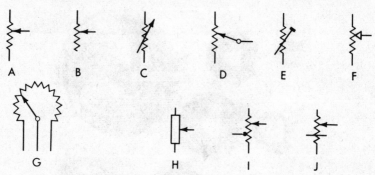

Fig. 2-9. Potentiometer and rheostat symbols.

The most popular code letter for designating a variable resistor is R. Some manufacturers, however, prefer the letter P (for potentiometer) or VR (for variable resistor).

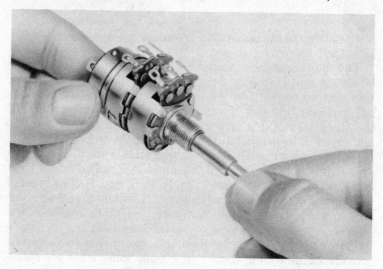

Courtesy of Clarostat Manufacturing Co., Inc.

Fig. 2-10. A two-section potentiometer with an on-off switch mounted on the rear.

Two potentiometers are sometimes constructed in one assembly, one unit being mounted behind the other. The shaft for one is hollow, allowing the shaft of the other unit to pass through it. This arrangement is quite common for certain TV controls; the operation is the same as for two separate units. The same code letter and number will often designate both units, with an A and B added to distinguish between them—such as R1A and R1B.

A switch may also be included on the back of potenti-ometers, as shown in Fig. 2-10. The same shaft which varies the resistance also actuates the switch. Electrically, however, there is no connection between the two.

SPECIAL RESISTORS

One of the most common of what might be called a "special" resistor is the fusible type. As its name implies, it acts as a fuse, opening the circuit if the current exceeds a certain limit. This protects expensive components against damage, and only a relatively inexpensive resistor must be replaced. Such units often are made to plug into a socket on the chassis, making replacement as simple as changing a tube. The symbols for such components are given in Fig. 2-11. Notice that the familiar resistor symbol is still used,

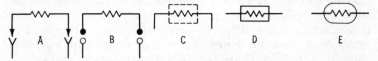

Fig. 2-11. Fusible-resistor symbols.

but with the plug-in arrangement indicated by an arrowhead or other appropriate designation. The fact that the unit is fusible is usually indicated by a notation near the symbol. Occasionally the conventional fuse symbol (see Chapter 8) is used for a fusible resistor.

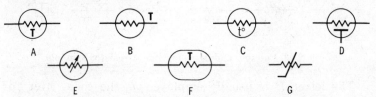

Fig. 2-12. Temperature-compensating resistor symbols.

Often there is a need for a special type of resistor which will vary in value when the conditions surrounding it or conditions in the circuit change. Many of these units are actually semiconductor devices (to be discussed in a later chapter); however, since they are used in a circuit to supply resistance, they will be given in this chapter.

As the temperature of a common resistor rises because of heat from surrounding components or from its own internal electron flow, the resistance of the resistor increases. To forestall this change, the composition of the resistor is altered to cause its resistance to decrease when the temperature increases. In fact, the change in resistance can be made to either increase, decrease, or remain constant regardless of the direction of temperature change (within limits, of course). These units are known as *temperature-compensating resistors, thermistors,* or *thermal resistors* (Fig. 2-12). If the resistance decreases as the temperature rises, they are said to have a *negative temperature coefficient* (NTC); if it increases, they have a *positive temperature coefficient* (PTC). The abbreviation signifying the type is usually placed beside the symbol.

Resistors are also available which vary in value according to the current through them or the voltage present in the circuit. Others vary in value when light strikes them. Often the same symbol shown at A in Fig. 2-12 is used for these resistors except the letter designating the type is changed to *V* for voltage, *I* for current, or *L* or λ for light. Other manufacturers use different symbols, however. In Fig. 2-13, symbols A through I are for voltage-dependent resistors; those in J through R are for light-dependent resistors.

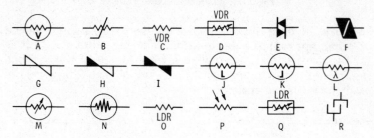

Fig. 2-13. Voltage- and light-dependent resistor symbols.

The letter *R* is usually employed as the code letter for voltage-, current-, temperature-, or light-dependent resistors. However, *RT* may be used for temperature-dependent resistors and *RV* for voltage-dependent resistors. In addition, *D* is sometimes used as the code letter for semiconductor-type resistors.

QUESTIONS

1. What is the unit of measurement for the amount of resistance?
2. What are the two main purposes of resistors?
3. What is resistance?
4. What Greek letter is used as the symbol for ohm?
5. What is a potentiometer?
6. What code letter is used for resistors?
7. What is the value of a resistor with red, violet, and orange bands?
8. What is a negative temperature-coefficient resistor?
9. Draw the symbol for a fixed resistor.
10. Draw the symbol for a tapped potentiometer.

CHAPTER 3

Capacitors

Like the resistor discussed in the previous chapter, the capacitor is found in nearly every electronic circuit. The term "condenser" was formerly used when referring to this unit, and will still be heard occasionally, but "capacitor" is now more universally accepted.

WHAT IS A CAPACITOR?

Basically, a capacitor is a device consisting of two plates of a conducting material separated by an insulator (Fig. 3-1). This arrangement gives it the property of being able to

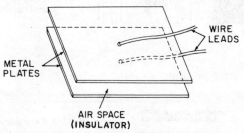

WIRE LEADS

METAL PLATES

AIR SPACE (INSULATOR)

Fig. 3-1. A basic capacitor.

store and release electrons as dictated by the external conditions affecting it. This storage and release is more commonly called *charge* and *discharge*.

CAPACITANCE

The property by which a capacitor is able to store electrons is called *capacitance*. The larger the plate area, the more electrons can be stored and hence the larger the capacitance. The unit of capacitance measurement is the *farad*. Since this unit is too large for ordinary work, the *microfarad* (one millionth of a farad) is more common. Microfarad is abbreviated mf, mfd, μf, or μfd. (The symbol μ is the Greek letter *mu*, the abbreviation for one millionth.) A still smaller unit, the picofarad (abbreviated pf or pfd) is sometimes encountered. This unit is equal to one millionth of one millionth of a farad, or one millionth of a microfarad. In other words:

1 pf = .000001 mfd = .000000000001 farad.

The term micromicrofarad (mmf, mmfd, $\mu\mu$f, or $\mu\mu$fd) was formerly used for picofarad and is still encountered quite often, but it is largely being replaced by the term "picofarad."

FIXED CAPACITORS

The capacitor shown in Fig. 3-1 is too large physically to be practical for most uses. If another insulating material is used instead of air, and if the plates are then rolled instead of lying flat, the unit can be made to occupy a much smaller

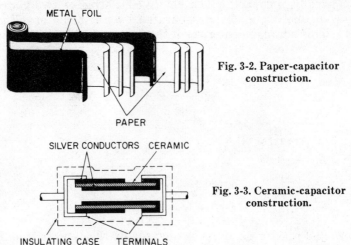

Fig. 3-2. Paper-capacitor construction.

Fig. 3-3. Ceramic-capacitor construction.

space. This method is shown in Fig. 3-2. This assembly can then be enclosed in plastic or wax-impregnated paper.

Other types of fixed capacitors have the plates arranged in layers separated by thin sheets of mica or other suitable material. Here again, the assembly can be encased in plastic. Fig. 3-3 shows the construction of a ceramic capacitor. The two metal plates (in this case, silver) are separated by a ceramic material and connected to the terminals at the end. These terminals, in turn, are connected to the leads.

Color Codes

Most fixed capacitors either will have their value stamped on them or will have a color code to give this and other information. Several different codes are used, the most popular being given in Fig. 3-4. (The capacity is always given in picofarads.)

In addition to the capacitance value, the working voltage is usually indicated also. This is the amount of voltage that can be continuously applied across the capacitor without its arcing and ruining the dielectric (insulating) material.

Symbols for fixed capacitors are shown in Fig. 3-5. The most popular is the one at A, having superseded B which was used for many years. Symbols C through G are for a special type of capacitor called a *feedthrough*. These units are either inserted through a hole in the chassis and soldered in place, or are screwed into a threaded hole. Typical feedthrough capacitors are pictured in Fig. 3-6.

Temperature Coefficient

Another rating often included in the color code is the *temperature coefficient*. Like resistors, capacitors often change in value when heated. To compensate for this, they can be manufactured so that their value will not vary at all, or will increase or decrease by predetermined amounts as the temperature changes. The temperature coefficient designates the amount of change in parts-per-million-per-degree centigrade. An N or a minus sign $(-)$ indicates a decrease in capacitance, and a P or a plus sign $(+)$, an increase.

ELECTROLYTIC CAPACITORS

Examples of another type of capacitor are shown in Fig. 3-7. These are called *electrolytics* because one plate consists

MOLDED PAPER CAPACITOR CODES
(Capacity Given In pf)

COLOR	DIGIT	MULTI-PLIER	TOLERANCE
BLACK	0	1	20%
BROWN	1	10	
RED	2	100	
ORANGE	3	1000	
YELLOW	4	10000	
GREEN	5	100000	5%
BLUE	6	1000000	
VIOLET	7		
GRAY	8		
WHITE	9		10%
GOLD			5%
SILVER			10%
NO COLOR			20%

MOLDED PAPER TUBULAR

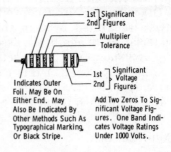

1st ⎤ Significant
2nd ⎦ Figures
Multiplier
Tolerance
1st ⎤ Significant
2nd ⎦ Voltage Figures

Indicates Outer Foil. May Be On Either End. May Also Be Indicated By Other Methods Such As Typographical Marking, Or Black Stripe.

Add Two Zeros To Significant Voltage Figures. One Band Indicates Voltage Ratings Under 1000 Volts.

MOLDED FLAT PAPER CAPACITORS
(COMMERCIAL CODE)

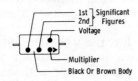

1st ⎤ Significant
2nd ⎦ Figures
Voltage
Multiplier
Black Or Brown Body

MOLDED FLAT PAPER CAPACITORS
(JAN CODE)

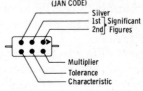

Silver
1st ⎤ Significant
2nd ⎦ Figures
Multiplier
Tolerance
Characteristic

MOLDED MICA CAPACITOR CODES
(Capacity Given In pf)

COLOR	DIGIT	MULTI-PLIER	TOLERANCE	CLASS OR CHARACTERISTIC
BLACK	0	1	20%	A
BROWN	1	10	1%	B
RED	2	100	2%	C
ORANGE	3	1000	3%	D
YELLOW	4	10000		E
GREEN	5		5% (EIA)	F(JAN)
BLUE	6			G(JAN)
VIOLET	7			
GRAY	8			I (EIA)
WHITE	9			J (EIA)
GOLD		.1	5%(JAN)	
SILVER		.01	10%	

Class or characteristic denotes specifications of design involving Q factors, temperature coefficients, and production test requirements.
All axial lead mica capacitors have a voltage rating of 300, 500, or 1000 volts.
* or ±1.0 pf whichever is greater

CURRENT STANDARD
JAN AND EIA CODE

White (EIA) Black (JAN)
1st ⎤ Significant
2nd ⎦ Figures
Multiplier
Tolerance
Class Or Characteristic

BUTTON SILVER MICA

1st (When Applicable)
2nd (or 1st)
3rd (or 2nd)
Multiplier
Tolerance
Class
Sig Fig

Fig. 3-4. Capacitor outline

CERAMIC CAPACITOR CODES (CAPACITY GIVEN IN pf)

COLOR	DIGIT	MULTI-PLIER	TOLERANCE 10 pf OR LESS	TOLERANCE OVER 10 pf	TEMPERATURE COEFFICIENT PPM/°C	EXTENDED RANGE TEMP. COEFF. SIGNIFICANT FIGURE	EXTENDED RANGE TEMP. COEFF. MULTIPLIER
BLACK	0	1	±2.0 pf	±20%	0(NPO)	0.0	-1
BROWN	1	10	±0.1 pf	±1%	-33(N033)		-10
RED	2	100		±2%	-75(N075)	1.0	-100
ORANGE	3	1000		±2.5%	-150(N150)	1.5	-1000
YELLOW	4	10000			-220(N220)	2.2	-10000
GREEN	5		±0.5 pf	±5%	-330(N330)	3.3	+1
BLUE	6				-470(N470)	4.7	+10
VIOLET	7				-750(N750)	7.5	+100
GRAY	8	.01	±0.25 pf		+30(P030)		+1000
WHITE	9	.1	±1.0 pf	±10%	General Purpose		+10000
SILVER					Bypass & Coupling		
GOLD					+100(P100) (JAN)		

Ceramic capacitor voltage ratings are standard 500 volts, for some manufacturers, 1000 volts for other manufacturers, unless otherwise specified.

HIGH CAPACITY TUBULAR CERMICS INSULATED OR NON-INSULATED

1st / 2nd Significant Figures
Multiplier
Tolerance
Voltage (Optional)

DISC CERAMICS (5-DOT SYSTEM)

1st / 2nd Significant Figures
Multiplier
Tolerance
Temperature Coefficient

BUTTON CERAMICS

1st / 2nd Significant Figures
Multiplier

Viewed From Soldered Surface

TEMPERATURE COMPENSATING TUBULAR CERAMICS

1st / 2nd Significant Figures
Multiplier
Tolerance
Temperature Coefficient

DISC CERAMICS (3-DOT SYSTEM)

1st / 2nd Significant Figures
Multiplier

STAND-OFF CERAMICS

1st / 2nd Significant Figures
Multiplier
Tolerance
Temperature Coefficient

EXTENDED RANGE T.C. TUBULAR CERAMICS

1st / 2nd Significant Figures
Multiplier
Tolerance
Temp. Coeff. Multiplier
T. C. Significant Figure

MOLDED-INSULATED AXIAL LEAD CERAMICS

1st / 2nd Significant Figures
Multiplier
Tolerance
Temperature Coefficient

FEED-THRU CERAMICS

1st / 2nd Significant Figures
Multiplier
Tolerance
Temperature Coefficient

MOLDED CERAMICS Using Standard Resistor Color-Code

1st / 2nd Significant Figures
Multiplier
Tolerance
White Band
Distinguishes Capacitor From Resistor

TYPOGRAPHICALLY MARKED CERAMICS

Temperature Coefficient
Capacity
Tolerance

NT50 100 K

JAN LETTER	TOLERANCE 10 pf OR LESS	TOLERANCE OVER 10 pf
C	±0.25 pf	
D	±0.5 pf	
F	±1.0 pf	±1%
G	±2.0 pf	±2%
J		±5%
K		±10%
M		±20%

drawings and color codes.

of a moist substance called an *electrolyte*. Certain metals—
aluminum is the most common—will have a thin oxide film
form on their surface when immersed in an electrolyte. This

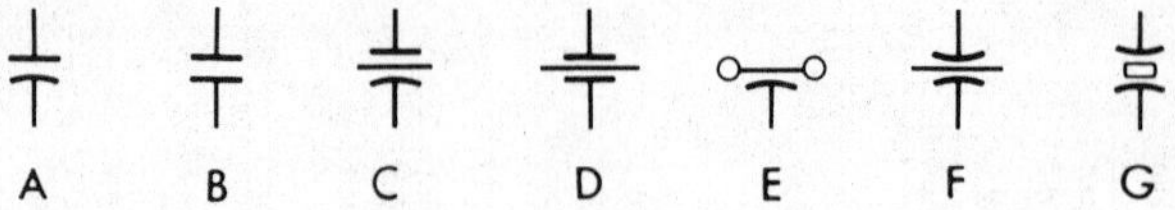

A   B   C   D   E   F   G

Fig. 3-5. Fixed-capacitor symbols.

oxide film becomes the insulation or dielectric between the
metal plate and the electrolyte which serves as the other
plate. Such capacitors are characterized by a high capacitance in comparison to their size.

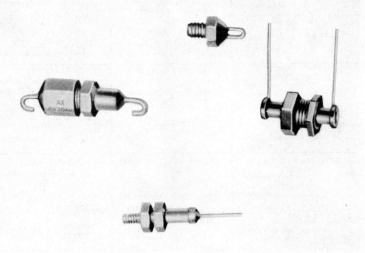

Courtesy Aerovox Corp.

Fig. 3-6. Four types of feedthrough capacitors.

Unlike other capacitors, electrolytics must usually be connected in the correct polarity. That is, the positive terminal
must go to the point with the most positive voltage, and the
other side to the most negative potential, usually ground.
Fig. 3-8 shows the symbols for designating electrolytics on
schematics. The same symbol used for regular capacitors
is sometimes employed. However, a plus sign or plus and
minus signs are usually added to indicate the proper polarity.
Symbol B is more popular, and here there is no doubt that it
is an electrolytic. Other electrolytic-capacitor symbols are
shown at C, D, and E.

More than one electrolytic capacitor is often enclosed in the same container. The negative side of all units will be connected together, but separate terminals or leads will be provided for the positive side of each. These multisection capacitors are sometimes designated by the symbols at B, C, and D—a separate symbol for each section. Occasionally the symbol at F, showing three sections, will be encountered.

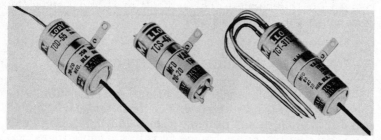

Fig. 3-7. Electrolytic capacitors.

The symbol at G is preferred by some manufacturers for a two-section capacitor. Notice the small rectangle and triangle near two sections in symbol F. Some units are enclosed in a metal can having twist prongs for mounting. The various sections are connected to terminals at the bottom, and small marks, such as a rectangle, triangle, or semicircle, are placed near them. These marks are stamped on the side of the can along with the respective value and voltage rating of each section, and are also included alongside the symbol in the schematic. These marks may also be included alongside any of the other symbols. Thus, they serve to identify the separate sections.

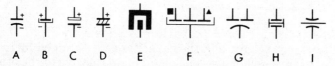

Fig. 3-8. Electrolytic-capacitor symbols.

Paper and other capacitors discussed previously will seldom have a value greater than 1 microfarad (it will usually be only a small fraction), whereas electrolytics will range from 1 to 200 microfarads or higher.

Because of their large values, electrolytics can store many more electrons. This makes them useful for smoothing out variations in voltage. They therefore find their widest application as filter capacitors in power supplies. Here, the voltage may vary over wide limits, but will always have the same polarity. Hence, the fact that electrolytics must be connected correctly, polaritywise, is not a hindrance.

In certain applications, however, a large capacitor is needed for a circuit in which the voltage does change polarity. Special *nonpolarized* electrolytic units have been developed for this purpose. The symbols at H and I show the designation for such a capacitor.

VARIABLE CAPACITORS

Just as a variable resistor is useful in some circuits, variable capacitors are also needed. The most familiar example is the tuning capacitor in many radios. As the tuning knob is rotated, the capacitor changes in value, causing its associated circuit to tune in the signal from the desired station.

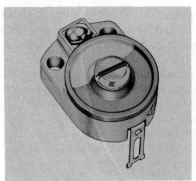

Fig. 3-9. A ceramic trimmer capacitor.

Courtesy Centralab, Electronics Div. of Globe-Union, Inc.

One type of variable capacitor is shown in Fig. 3-9. Its dielectric is ceramic and the capacitance is changed by turning a screw which moves one metal plate relative to the other. This so-called "trimmer" is usually designated by symbols A or B in Fig. 3-10. The arrowhead in A signifies that the capacitance of the unit is variable. The symbol at B signifies a preset adjustment. That is, once set it is not normally adjusted except for alignment.

Another type of variable capacitor is illustrated in Fig. 3-11. Here, two sets of plates, each consisting of several flat pieces of metal connected together, mesh as the shaft is turned. Air is the dielectric, and if the shaft is rotated so the

40

movable set of plates (called the *rotor*) is entirely surrounded by the stationary set (called the *stator*), the capacitance will be maximum. If rotated so the rotor extends out of the stator, it will be minimum.

The symbols for a trimmer capacitor may also be used for the unit just described, although the symbols shown at C, D, E, and F in Fig. 3-10 are often employed. The arrow is used

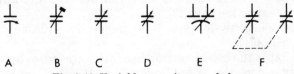

A   B   C   D   E   F

Fig. 3-10. Variable-capacitor symbols.

in various ways to designate a variable capacitance. For example, symbol E signifies a split rotor; that is, the stator plates are divided into two separate sections, but the rotor plates are not.

Fig. 3-11. A two-gang variable tuning capacitor.

The capacitor pictured in Fig. 3-11 is actually two separate units connected together mechanically by a single shaft. The larger unit tunes one section of a radio, and the smaller unit another section. Rotating the shaft changes the capacitance of each unit simultaneously. This type is called a *ganged* capacitor and is usually designated by the symbol at F in Fig. 3-10. The dashed line between the arrows signifies that both sections are mechanically connected.

CODE LETTERS

Nearly all fixed and variable capacitors are designated by the code letter *C* (one manufacturer uses *E* for electrolytics). The letters *M*, *E*, or *VC* are sometimes employed to signify variable units.

QUESTIONS

1. What is the primary purpose of a capacitor?
2. Do electrons flow through a capacitor connected to an AC voltage?
3. What is the basic unit for measuring the electrical size of a capacitor?
4. What is the insulating material between the two sides of a capacitor called?
5. Are electrolytic capacitors generally suitable for AC circuits?
6. What is the most common use for electrolytic capacitors?
7. What does the prefix "micro" mean?
8. What is the movable portion of a tuning capacitor called?
9. What is the most common code letter for capacitors?
10. Identify the types of capacitors signified by the following symbols.

    (A) ⊣⊢   (B) ⊣⊢   (C) ⊣⊪

CHAPTER 4

Coils and Transformers

Just as any circuit or even a length of wire contains resistance and capacitance, it also will contain inductance—the electrical property of a coil.

WHAT IS A COIL?

A coil, or *inductor* as it is sometimes called, in its simplest form is just what its name implies—a wire wound into the shape of a coil. To be useful, however, coils must be wound in a certain way so that they will have the proper inductance value.

When current flows through a conductor, magnetic lines of force will be generated and will occupy the surrounding space. As long as the current is steady, the magnetic field will remain stationary, but if the current varies, the magnetic field will do likewise. Should the current stop suddenly (be shut off), the lines of force will collapse.

Whenever magnetic lines of force cross a conductor, an electric current is generated. Thus, the magnetic field produced by the current flowing in one turn of a coil will cut across other turns, setting up a current in them. This is repeated for each turn in the coil. The over-all effect, when the current is made to increase, decrease, or change direction, is that the coil tends to oppose these changes. In other words, it tries to "smooth out" variations in current. A steady current (DC) will have no opposition except for the small resistance of the wire itself.

The electrical property of a coil is called *inductance*. The basic unit of measurement is the *henry* (abbreviated h), but like the farad, smaller units are often needed. The *millihenry* (mh), equal to one-thousandth of a henry, and the *microhenry* (μh), equal to one-millionth of a henry, are the more common units for specifying inductance values.

AIR-CORE COILS

The simplest coil has an air-core and is constructed by winding a wire into a series of loops. The more usual method, however, is to wind the wire onto a plastic, paper, or other nonmetallic form. As long as this form is not capable of being magnetized (not a conductor of magnetic lines of force), the effect is the same as if no form were employed.

The two air-core coils shown in Fig. 4-1 are wound on a phenolic form. The symbols used for air-core coils are given in Fig. 4-2. The loops will usually be shown open as in A, although some manufacturers prefer the simpler symbol at B.

Courtesy of Merit Coil and Transformer Corp.

Fig. 4-1. Two types of air-core coils.

Air-core coils may or may not be color coded. In any case, the value is usually given either next to the symbol on the schematic or in the parts list, and will always be in the millihenry or microhenry range—never in henrys.

44

The code letter L is practically universal for coils of all types. The letters RFC (meaning Radio-Frequency Choke) or the letter X may sometimes be used.

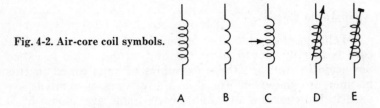

Fig. 4-2. Air-core coil symbols.

Adjustable Air-Core Coils

It is often desirable to change the inductance of a coil. This can be done by making the coil adjustable. Symbols for this type are shown at C, D, and E. It can also be represented by adding the adjustable symbol to the symbol at B. The symbol at C is often used to depict a coil having a slider that moves along the turns to "switch in" the desired portion. D may be used to indicate a coil in which the inductance is changed by either compressing or expanding the turns to change the spacing between them. Both symbols are interchangeable, however.

POWDERED-IRON CORE COILS

Other types of coils have cores of ferrite or powdered iron (called iron-dust in some parts of the world). Ferrites are made by molding powdered iron or a similar substance into

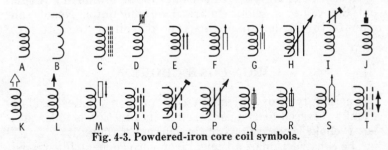

Fig. 4-3. Powdered-iron core coil symbols.

the desired shape. When such a core is brought near or inserted into a coil, it offers a more convenient path for the magnetic lines of force than does air. Hence, more lines cut the other conductors in the coil, increasing the inductance. The same symbols used for the air-core type—A and B in

45

Fig. 4-3—may also be used for powdered-iron core coils. The symbol at C is also popular. The core may be represented by either two or three dashed lines.

Adjustable Cores

To change the inductance of powdered-iron core coils, the core is usually moved in or out of the unit. This is called *permeability* tuning; three examples of coils tuned in this manner are shown in Fig. 4-4. Many types of symbols are used to indicate the adjustable core. Some are shown at D through T in Fig. 4-3. Notice that most follow the same pattern of showing an arrow, but in a different manner.

Fig. 4-4. Permeability-tuned coils.

Courtesy Triad Distributor Division, Litton Industries

Most permeability-tuned coils are in the millihenry range, but the value is seldom marked on the units. Nearly all manufacturers designate this type of coil by the letter *L*.

IRON-CORE CHOKES

Another type of coil has a core of iron or steel and is usually referred to as a *choke*, since its function is to smooth out ("choke") variations in the current through it.

The construction of a typical iron-core choke is illustrated in Fig. 4-5. Instead of the core being a solid piece of metal, it is usually constructed from a series of thin sheets, or *laminations* (visible at the center of the figure). Insulated wire is wound in layers around the core, each layer being separated by additional insulation (usually paper). These layers

46

may be left exposed, or the entire unit may be enclosed in a steel shell. Coils of this type are able to provide a large amount of inductance, usually in the henry range.

Fig. 4-5. Cutaway view of an iron-core transformer.

Courtesy Merit Coil and Transformer Corp.

The symbols for iron-core chokes are given at A, B, C, D, and E in Fig. 4-6. Note that they are the same as for other types of coils except that two or three solid lines are added to indicate the iron core. (The closed-loop symbol at D can be used for any of the core designations shown with open loops.) The symbols at F and G are for tapped units—that is, connections to different points on the winding permit particular portions or sections of the coil to be used.

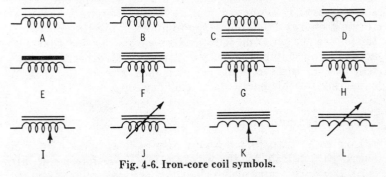

Fig. 4-6. Iron-core coil symbols.

Adjustable iron-core chokes are comparatively rare. Usually, instead of being continuously variable, a series of taps and a switch are employed to make connection to the desired portion. When a continuously variable iron-core unit is used, however, it may be indicated by any one of the

47

symbols at H, I, J, K, or L. These are the same as for a conventional choke, but with an arrow added to signify the inductance can be varied.

The letter *L* is usually used to indicate an iron-core choke, although occasionally *FC* (filter choke) is used.

TRANSFORMERS

A transformer is merely two or more coils positioned in such a manner that the magnetic field produced as a result of current flowing through one winding will cut across the other winding or windings. When this happens, a current will be *induced* in these other windings, even though they are not physically connected to the first.

The winding connected to the voltage source is called the *primary*. Any other winding is called a *secondary*. Besides causing a current flow in the secondary, the transformer can also change the amount of voltage. If the number of turns on both the primary and secondary are equal, then the voltage across each will be the same. With more turns on the secondary than on the primary, the secondary voltage will be higher. Conversely, if the secondary has fewer turns, its voltage will be lower.

Thus, the main function of a transformer is either to transfer an AC voltage from the primary to the secondary, or to step the voltage up or down. In either case the current in the secondary will vary exactly in step with the current in the primary. This phenomenon is used in *coupling*, or transferring, energy from one stage to another. Adding a capacitor across the winding will produce a combination that will accept a particular frequency and exclude all others. Current will flow in the secondary (which may also be *tuned* by a capacitor) at this particular frequency only.

Types of Transformers

Like coils, transformers may also have either air or iron cores. Fig. 4-7 shows the symbols for those having an air core. Air-core transformers usually are not variable, since

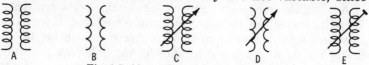

Fig. 4-7. Air-core transformer symbols.

the only way this can be done is to move one of the coils with respect to the other. If this is done, however, symbols shown by C, D, and E are used.

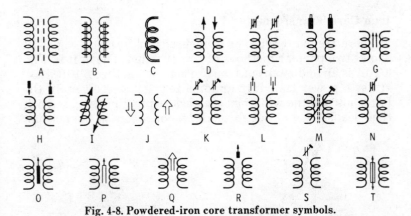

Fig. 4-8. Powdered-iron core transformer symbols.

Fig. 4-8 shows the symbols for designating a powdered-iron core transformer. In this type the individual coils are usually wound on a single form (Fig. 4-9). In Fig. 4-9A the unit is shielded by a metal cover (called a *can*); the one in Fig. 4-9B has no such covering. Both units have capacitors connected across their windings for tuning.

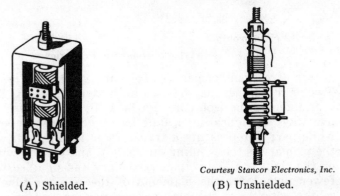

Courtesy Stancor Electronics, Inc.

(A) Shielded.   (B) Unshielded.

Fig. 4-9. Two types of permeability-tuned transformers.

A special winding, called a *bifilar*, is sometimes indicated by the symbol at C in Fig. 4-8. In this type of unit the conductors for both windings are placed side by side and wound on the form together.

49

The symbols at D through L in Fig. 4-8 usually are employed to indicate that each winding is separately tunable, while the symbols at M through T indicate the tuning adjustment affects both windings simultaneously.

Iron-Core Transformers

There are many types of iron-core transformers. Fig. 4-10 shows two popular methods of construction. The unit in Fig. 4-10A is an audio-output transformer, while Fig. 4-10B illustrates a power transformer for a television receiver. In the latter unit all the windings are enclosed in a metal case with their leads brought out through two openings in the bottom.

Courtesy Stancor Electronics, Inc.

(A) Audio output.   (B) Power.

Fig. 4-10. Two types of iron-core transformers.

Iron-core transformer symbols are given in Fig. 4-11. Two or three lines may be used in the symbols at A, B, and C to indicate the iron core. Parts A, B, C, D, and E show five ways of indicating a unit having only two windings, while part F represents a transformer having four. Here, the primary is the winding on the left, and the top winding on the right is a low-voltage secondary (as signified by the fewer turns) for the filaments of the rectifier tube. The center winding is the high-voltage portion and is center-tapped. The winding at the bottom is for the filaments of all other tubes in the receiver.

A special type of transformer, called an *autotransformer*, is symbolized at G. The portion from one end to the tap acts as one winding, and the complete coil, from one end to the

50

other, acts as the other winding. Such units can step the voltage either up or down, and may have taps from which different voltages can be obtained.

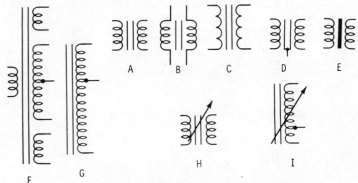

Fig. 4-11. Iron-core transformer symbols.

The symbols at H and I indicate variable iron-core transformers. Like the iron-core chokes, these types are seldom encountered. Tapped windings are usually employed instead.

The code letter *T* is almost universal for the designation of iron-core transformers. The letter *L* will sometimes be used, however, to indicate air- and powdered-iron–core transformers and *AOT* may be used to signify an audio-output transformer.

QUESTIONS

1. What is the electrical property of a coil called?
2. What is the unit of measurement of the property in Question 1?
3. What effect does a coil have on steady DC flowing through it?
4. What enables one winding of a transformer to couple a current in another winding?
5. What is used to signify an iron core on a coil or transformer?
6. What is the more common name for an iron-core coil?
7. What is the name of the transformer winding in which the incoming current flows?
8. What do two or three rows of dashed lines between the windings of a transformer indicate?
9. What code letters are used to designate transformers?
10. Draw the symbol for an air-core coil.

CHAPTER 5

Electron Tubes

The entire foundation of electronics is based on the tiny, negatively-charged particle called an *electron*. These electrons will flow from a negative to a positive voltage source if a complete conductive path is provided. This flow constitutes an electron current. Unless it can be controlled in some way, however, it will serve no useful purpose. Electron tubes are one type of device used to control this flow.

DIODE TUBES

Fig. 5-1 shows the elementary construction of the simplest of electron tubes—the *diode*. A length of special resistance

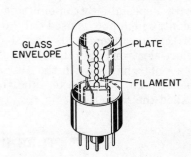

Fig. 5-1. Construction of a diode tube.

wire, placed in the center of the unit, becomes hot when current flows through it. This heat causes electrons to be expelled from the surface of the wire (called the *filament*) into the surrounding vacuum. (The entire tube is evacuated of air, because the presence of oxygen would cause the fila-

53

ment to burn up.) Separated from the filament by the vacuum is another element, the *plate* (sometimes called the *anode*). If this plate is connected to a positive voltage source, the electrons "boiled off" the filament will flow toward it. If the voltage on this element is less positive than the filament, however, it will not attract electrons and no current will flow.

An alternating voltage (AC) placed on the plate will cause electrons to flow only during the time this element is more positive than the filament—not while it is more negative. Hence, we have the first control action of a tube—changing an AC voltage (on the plate) into a pulsating DC (on the filament). This action is called *rectification*. The pulsating DC is then smoothed out by an electrolytic capacitor.

Fig. 5-2. Diode tube symbols.

The symbol for this type of tube is given at A in Fig. 5-2. The circle represents the glass or metal envelope, the pointed portion at the bottom of the circle is the filament, and the straight horizontal bar with the vertical line extending upward is the plate.

Another type of diode tube is indicated by symbol B. Here, an additional element called the *cathode* is placed between the filament and plate. This element is a metal sleeve, coated with a special electron-emitting material. It fits over the filament, which now is used only to furnish heat. The advantage of this arrangement is that the heated cathode can produce more electrons than the filament and, in addition, its emission does not change with the alternating current often used to heat it. In this type of tube the filament is more properly called the *heater*.

TUBE BASES

Connections are made from the elements of the tube to pins in its base. The most popular bases for modern tubes are the 7- and 9-pin miniature and the 8-pin octal. In the 7- and 9-pin types, the pins are merely symmetrically-spaced wires which extend through the bottom of the glass envelope. A blank space between two of the pins serves as a guide for inserting the tube into the socket. In an octal-base tube, wires from the tube elements pass through the glass envelope and are soldered to pins embedded in a plastic or phenolic base. A keyed center post on the base serves to guide the tube into its socket.

There are many other base arrangements. Most will have a blank space, locating key, or other provision for orienting the tube in the socket. In some tubes, all pins are not connected to elements. In fact, some pins may even be omitted from the base if a locating key is employed.

Each pin is numbered for reference purposes. With the base pointed toward you, pin 1 is the first pin starting clockwise from the blank space or locating key. All other pins are numbered consecutively, reading clockwise around the base. (If a pin is omitted, the number ordinarily assigned to it is skipped, but the location of the other pins remains the same.)

These pin numbers are also placed on schematics next to the tube symbol, at the point where the respective tube elements enter the tube envelope. When this type of symbol is used, it is known as a *basing diagram*. By referring to the numbers beside the elements, you can locate the pin connected to each element.

Fig. 5-3. A diode tube with a plate cap.

In some tubes the connection to an element will be brought out the top to a cap instead of to a pin on the base. The cap is almost always connected to the plate. (In pre-World War II tubes it was often connected to another element called the grid.) A cap is usually symbolized by a small box around the lead, at the point where it enters the tube envelope. This is shown in Fig. 5-3, along with the pin numbers of the filaments.

TRIODE TUBES

The diode tube discussed previously performed only one control action—it converted an AC current to a pulsating DC current. The widest function of tubes, however, is to amplify a signal (i.e., make it greater). The diode tube cannot do this; in fact, it actually causes a slight reduction in

55

signal strength. For amplification, at least one more element must be added between the cathode and plate, as shown by the drawing of a triode, or 3-element tube in Fig. 5-4. The

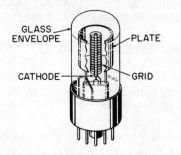

GLASS ENVELOPE
PLATE
CATHODE
GRID

Fig. 5-4. Construction of a triode tube.

added element, a cylinder made of fine-wire mesh, is called the *control grid*. This grid is represented by the dashed line between the cathode and plate in symbol A of Fig. 5-5.

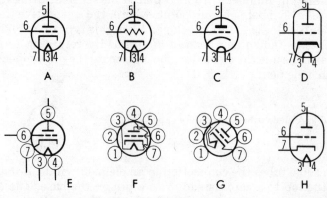

A   B   C   D

E   F   G   H

Fig. 5-5. Triode tube symbols.

In this type of tube, electrons will flow from cathode to plate, but they must first pass through the intervening control grid. Like the plate, the control grid is able to regulate the electron flow from the cathode—the more positive the control grid, the greater the electron flow, and vice versa. Being closer to the cathode, it exerts more influence than the plate, however.

TUBE VOLTAGES

The cathode—or in filament-type tubes, the minus side of the filament—is the reference point of all voltages in the tube since it emits the electrons. The cathode is connected either directly, or through a resistor, to this common reference point, generally referred to as simply *ground*. Hence the cathode voltage is either zero, or at most, slightly positive.

The grid is usually a few volts negative with respect to the cathode. Recall that a negative voltage will repel the electrons as they attempt to flow through the tube. However, electrons will still flow through the openings in the grid structure unless the voltage applied to it is too negative. Then, the grid repels all the electrons back to the cathode and the tube is said to be *cut off*. As the grid becomes less negative, however, more electrons will be drawn through it by the positive potential on the plate. If the grid becomes positive with respect to the cathode, it will also attract the electrons, and they will flow in the grid circuit.

As you can see, the electron flow of the plate will alternately increase and decrease if a varying voltage, such as an AC signal, is applied to the grid. These increases and decreases in the amount of electron flow through the plate resistor will cause much larger voltage variations at the plate than those of the grid signal which caused them.

SYMBOLS

The symbols used by most manufacturers to denote tubes are all very similar. Formerly, the symbol at B in Fig. 5-5 was used in which the zigzag line denoted the grid. It is seldom encountered today, however. The circle denoting the envelope is sometimes omitted, especially in pencil sketches.

Another way of showing the cathode and heater is given at C. Here, the cathode and filament are both curved. Also notice that the shape of the plate has been changed slightly. Another method of denoting the cathode is given at D.

Probably the major discrepancy in tube symbols is in the method of showing the pin or base connections. One method was shown in Fig. 5-3 and again in A and B of Fig. 5-5. Other ways of designating the bases are given at E, F, and G. These symbols show circles spaced around the tube envelope with the pin numbers inside. These numbers are arranged in the same order and in the same position as they actually appear on the base at F and G, with the various elements inside the envelope shown connected to their respective pins. The elements within the tube are sometimes tilted as in G. Any of the symbols in Fig. 5-5 may be lying on their side, or even upside down. The envelope may be elongated, as shown at D and H, instead of being shown as a circle. In each case, however, the basic symbol remains the same. These variations will not always be mentioned in the following sections of this chapter, but remember that they may exist.

TETRODE TUBES

In Chapter 3 it was stated that a capacitive effect would exist between two conductors separated by an insulator. In the previously discussed triode tube, a certain amount of capacitance exists between the grid and plate. This *inter-electrode capacitance*, as it is called, is detrimental to circuit operation in certain applications. To reduce its value, a fourth element, called a *screen grid*, can be placed between the grid and plate. Such a tube is called a *tetrode*, and its symbol is shown in Fig. 5-6. Notice the additional element, which looks exactly like the control grid in the drawing. In

Fig. 5-6. Symbol for a tetrode tube.

fact, its physical construction is very similar, but unlike the control grid, it is connected to a high positive voltage. A by-pass capacitor, usually connected from the screen grid to common ground, makes this element appear at neutral (ground) to any signal voltage in the tube. As a result, the shielding action of the screen greatly reduces the effect of the capacitance between the control grid and plate. In addition, tetrode tubes are characterized by a much higher gain (provide more amplification) than can be obtained from a triode.

PENTODE TUBES

The tetrode tube would seem to be ideal, since it overcomes the disadvantage of the interelectrode capacitance found in a triode, and at the same time gives more amplification. But its effectiveness is limited by another phenomenon known as *secondary emission*. As the electrons from the cathode strike the plate, some of them bounce off and some of the electrons already on the surface of the plate are also knocked loose. All these are attracted by the positive potential on the screen.

Thus, the screen grid receives more than its share of electrons while the plate, which is the intended destination of the electrons, receives less. As a result, more electrons flow in the screen circuit (known as screen current) and fewer in the plate circuit (plate current).

The effect of secondary emission can be overcome by adding another element, similar in construction to the control and screen grids, between the screen and plate. This element is called the *suppressor* grid, and the type of tube in which it appears is called a *pentode*. The suppressor is connected to either the cathode or ground. Recall that a positive voltage is a point where there is a deficiency of electrons, and that a negative voltage is a point where there is an excess. The suppressor grid, having far more electrons than the plate, repels the secondary-emission·electrons back to the plate before they have an opportunity to reach the screen grid.

Fig. 5-7. Symbol for a pentode tube.

The symbol for the pentode tube is shown in Fig. 5-7. Notice that it is the same as the symbol for the tetrode except for an additional grid between the plate and screen.

BEAM-POWER TUBES

The *beam-power* tube is often thought of as being a pentode, although its operation is more like that of the tetrode. Fig. 5-8 shows its symbol. Instead of a suppressor grid, it

Fig. 5-8. Symbol for a beam-power tube.

has two metal vanes (called *beam-forming plates*) positioned in such a way as to guide or focus the electrons toward the plate (Fig. 5-9). In addition, the wires of the screen and control grids are in line, permitting more electrons to flow through. In this way, the tube can deliver much greater power.

The beam-forming plates are connected to the cathode inside the tube. The regular tetrode (Fig. 5-6) or pentode (Fig.

5-7) symbol is sometimes used for the beam-power tube. In either instance, a tube manual will have to be consulted to determine whether or not the tube in question is a beam-power type.

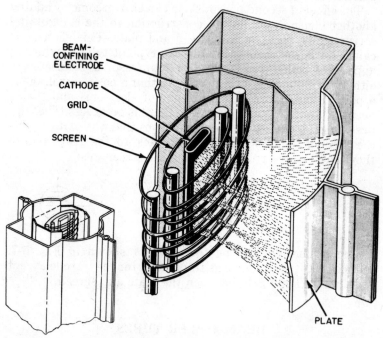

BEAM-CONFINING ELECTRODE

CATHODE

GRID

SCREEN

PLATE

Fig. 5-9. Construction of beam-power tube.

PENTAGRID TUBES

Fig. 5-10 shows the symbol for a *pentagrid* tube. It has a total of five grids between the cathode and plate, and performs two functions in a radio. The first is that of the local oscillator, a stage which generates a high-frequency signal.

Fig. 5-10. Symbol for a pentagrid tube.

The first grid acts as the oscillator grid and the second as the plate. Electrons will flow on through it, however, toward the conventional plate of the tube. The third grid acts as the control grid for the remainder of the tube. This portion is similar to a conventional pentode and has the signal from the antenna applied to its grid. The electron stream is already varying in accordance with the oscillator frequency when it reaches the third grid. The two signals (from the oscillator and antenna) beat together, or *heterodyne,* producing a new signal which varies in the same manner as the signal applied to the third grid, but has a frequency equal to the difference between the two signals. This action is called *mixing.* The fourth grid (connected to the second) functions as the screen for the pentode section, and the fifth functions as the suppressor.

DUAL-SECTION TUBES

Two or more tube functions are often combined in a single envelope. Some of the more popular combinations are: two diodes; two triodes; two diodes and a triode or pentode; and a triode and pentode. The elements for both tubes are sometimes drawn side by side in the symbol, as shown at A in Fig. 5-11. The dashed line through the center represents a shield placed between the two sections to prevent interaction. Some tubes do not have this shield. If the two halves are in separate circuits they will usually be drawn as shown at B. Here, the dotted line at one side signifies that there is another section of the tube. Symbol C, with the dotted lines omitted and the side left open, will sometimes be used instead. You may occasionally find schematics in which one half of a dual-section tube will be completely enclosed within the circle, exactly like the single-section tube shown previously. The parts list will usually indicate that the tube is a dual-section type, or if not, a tube manual can be consulted.

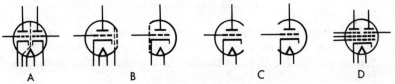

Fig. 5-11. Dual-section tube symbols.

Another type of dual tube is depicted by symbol D. Here the tube is actually a dual-pentode, except that the same cathode, control grid, and screen grid serve (are common to) both sections. In other tubes only the cathode may be shared. If so, and if each section is drawn at a different place on the schematic, the cathode will be shown in both places but the same pin number will be placed beside the cathode symbol.

In some dual-section tubes the filament is tapped in the center so that it can be operated from either 6 or 12 volts. Two filament connections will be shown in one half of the tube and one in the other half, as depicted by symbol B of Fig. 5-11. An untapped filament will be shown by symbol C. Here, one side of the filament connection is given in each section. The filament is shown in each half, as in a single-section tube, but only one line extends beyond the envelope.

GAS-FILLED TUBES

Instead of being evacuated, certain tubes are filled with a gas. Some tubes of this type require no filament voltage—hence are called *cold-cathode* or *ionically-heated cathode* tubes. Symbol A in Fig. 5-12 is for a cold-cathode diode tube. Notice that instead of a flat bar, a circle is used to represent the cathode, and no filament is shown. Sometimes this circle is replaced by a dot, as at B. In either symbol, a smaller dot, indicating a gas-filled tube, also appears inside the envelope. The other connection shown inside symbol B is a wire between two pins on the tube base. Its purpose is to open another circuit when the tube is removed. This protects the equipment if accidentally turned on with the tube out of the socket.

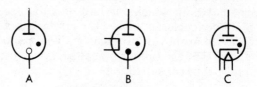

A   B   C

Fig. 5-12. Gas-tube symbols.

The symbol for another type of gas-filled tube, called a *thyratron,* is given at C. It is the same as the symbol for a triode except for the dot inside the envelope. The thyratron is used in certain control applications.

PHOTOTUBES

Symbol A in Fig. 5-13 depicts a different type of tube. Certain materials—potassium, sodium, and cesium, for example—give off small quantities of electrons when exposed to light. A curved piece of metal with a coating of this photosensitive material acts as the cathode. The plate (anode) is a metal rod in front of it. When light strikes the photosensitive material, electrons are released and flow to the plate. In the symbol, the curved portion represents the cathode, and the flat bar (or a dot or circle) represents the plate (usually called the anode in a phototube).

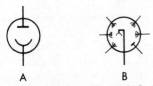

A   B

Fig. 5-13. Phototube symbols.

The symbol for another type of phototube, called a *photomultiplier*, is shown at B. The main cathode is the curved element at the center from which electrons flow to the first element at the bottom left of the symbol. This element, in turn, emits more electrons to the next similar element. (Notice that the symbol for the elements around the outside of the tube are a combination of the photocathode and anode symbols.) These elements attract the electrons, and each in turn emits more electrons than the preceding one, until finally the element to the right of the cathode lead is reached. Here, the conventional anode symbol is used for the element from which the output is taken. Because of this multiplier action, many more electrons flow from the output than could flow from the tube at A.

ELECTRON-RAY TUBES

The *electron-ray*, or *tuning-eye*, tube is used on some radios and tuners to indicate when the set is tuned exactly on station, and with tape recorders to indicate the recording level.

The simplest tuning eye is essentially a triode with two electrodes added, as shown by symbol A in Fig. 5-14. The slanted element is called the *target*. Electrons emitted by the cathode strike this target and cause it to fluoresce (glow). The other element is the *deflector*, or *ray-control electrode*— a thin vertical vane placed between the cathode and target. As shown by the symbol, the deflector is connected to the triode plate and causes a shadow to fall on the target. When the set is tuned exactly on the station frequency, the shortest shadow is cast. As the signal strength decreases, the shadow lengthens.

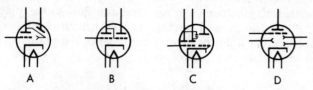

Fig. 5-14. Electron-ray tube symbols.

Some other symbols for depicting tuning-eye tubes are given at B, C, and D. All employ the same principle—that of a deflector casting a shadow on the target.

CATHODE-RAY TUBES

Cathode-ray tubes are usually classified according to whether they employ electrostatic or electromagnetic deflection. The principal use for the former is in oscilloscopes, while the television picture tube is the most familiar application for the latter.

Electrostatic Deflection

Fig. 5-15 shows the construction of a typical electrostatic tube. The electrons leave the heated cathode, as in other tubes, and are attracted by the positive voltage on the accelerating

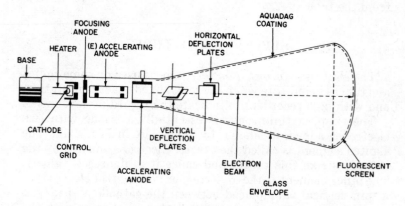

Fig. 5-15. Construction of an electrostatically-deflected cathode-ray tube.

anode. First, however, they must flow through the control grid, a metal cylinder with a hole in one end. A negative voltage on this element controls the number of electrons allowed to pass through. From the control grid, the electrons pass on to the focus anode, which concentrates them into a narrow beam that strikes the screen in a small, sharply defined area. After the electrons leave the focusing anode, their velocity is increased by two high-voltage accelerating anodes.

The remaining electrodes are the deflection plates. The two horizontal plates move the beam from side to side across the screen, and the vertical-deflection plates move it up and down.

After passing through and being influenced by the deflection plates, the beam strikes the screen with great force, causing a fluorescent coating on the screen to glow. The brightness depends on the number of electrons and their velocity.

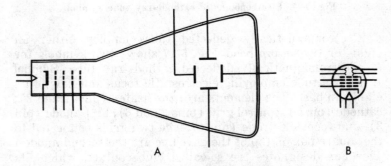

Fig. 5-16. Electrostatic cathode-ray tube symbols.

Symbol A in Fig. 5-16 is sometimes used to depict an electrostatic cathode-ray tube. (Note its similarity to the tube.) The elements are shown in the order in which they appear in the tube—from left to right they are the heater, cathode, control grid, focusing electrode, and accelerating anodes. The deflection plates are drawn in the form of a square.

At other times the symbol for the electrostatic cathode-ray tube resembles that of a conventional tube, as shown at B. Notice that here the focus electrode is placed between two sections of the accelerating anode. Where other arrangements are used, the schematic symbol shows the actual arrangement of the elements. The deflecting plates are represented by the four pointed electrodes at the top of the tube in symbol B.

Electromagnetically Deflected Cathode-Ray Tubes

The most familiar type of electromagnetically deflected cathode-ray tube is the one in your television tube, except it has no deflection plates. Instead, the beam is deflected both horizontally and vertically by coils around the neck of the tube. Often there are no focusing electrodes either; the electron beam is converged on the screen by a permanent magnet or an electromagnet around the neck.

A   B

Fig. 5-17. Electromagnetic cathode-ray tube symbols.

Electromagnetically deflected tubes employ either an eight- or twelve-pin base. Fig. 5-17 shows two symbols for an electromagnetically deflected cathode-ray tube. Symbol A is for a tube employing electrostatic focus and having an eight-pin base. The elements are: the heater (pins 1 and 8), cathode (pin 7), control grid (pins 2 and 6), first anode (pin 3), and focus electrode (pin 4). The two grids connected to the square box on top of the envelope are the second anodes. This box designates the so-called bulb contact, which fits through the side of the tube. The small capacitor, shown inside the tube and connected to the box labeled *C*, designates the capacitance between the coatings placed on both sides of the glass envelope. These coatings, called the *aquadag*, act as a capacitor to filter the high voltage connected to the bulb contact. Symbol B shows a twelve-pin electromagnetically focused tube; hence, no focus elements are included.

Another symbol for a cathode-ray tube is shown at A in Fig. 5-18. Here, the symbol resembles the actual construction of the tube. The elements, from top to bottom, are the heater, control grid, first anode, and second anode. A variation of symbol A is shown at B. Here, the symbol has been simplified by showing the tube neck broken at the bottom, and leaving the base pins off the top. This symbol is for an eight-pin, electrostatically focused tube. Still another method of symbolizing a cathode-ray tube is given at C.

66

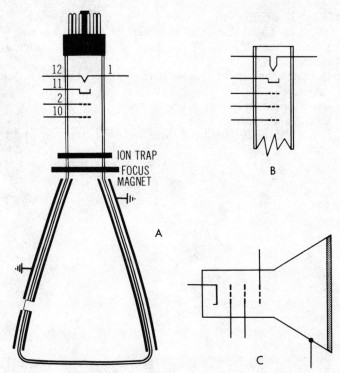

Fig. 5-18. Other types of symbols used for electromagnetic cathode-ray tubes.

CODE LETTERS

Manufacturers are almost unanimous in selecting the letter V (for vacuum) to designate all types of tubes (vacuum or gas) on their schematics. One manufacturer, however, chooses to designate the socket, instead of the tube itself, by using the letter S. The letter T is also employed occasionally; but most save it for designating transformers, as discussed in a previous chapter.

QUESTIONS

1. What is the primary purpose of all electron tubes?
2. What is the purpose of the cathode in an electron tube?
3. What is the most common letter used to designate tubes on schematics?

4. What is a cold-cathode tube?
5. What is the most common type of cathode-ray tube?
6. From what element of the tube is the output normally taken?
7. How are connections made to the various elements inside the tube?
8. Draw the symbol for a triode tube.
9. Draw a thyratron tube.
10. Draw a dual-section tube; one section a pentode, and the other a triode.

CHAPTER 6

Semiconductors

The primary purpose of *semiconductors*, or *solid-state* devices as they are sometimes called, is to control the flow of electrons. They can be employed in almost any application that a tube can, and in some where a tube cannot.

WHAT IS A SEMICONDUCTOR?

When properly treated, certain materials such as germanium, silicon, and selenium have the unique property of allowing electrons to flow through them in one direction, but not in the other. They therefore act like a conductor in one direction, but like an insulator in the other. Hence the name, "semiconductor." Unlike vacuum tubes, the semiconductor material is solid—there is no need to separate the various parts by a vacuum or gas. In some, the entire unit is composed of the same type of material. In others, the materials are different but are still in physical contact with each other. Connections are then made at the proper places, and a protective covering placed over the entire assembly.

RECTIFIERS

The power rectifier is the simplest and oldest of the semiconductor devices. It performs essentially the same function as a diode tube. In the power supplies of radio and television receivers, for example, it converts the AC line voltage into the DC needed to operate the various stages. The oldest type of metallic rectifier used in entertainment-type

Fig. 6-1. A selenium rectifier.

equipment is made of selenium, a typical unit of which is pictured in Fig. 6-1. The desired rating is determined by the number of plates. Two other types of selenium rectifiers are pictured in Fig. 6-2. Each of these units actually contains four separate power rectifiers connected together. Note their small size.

Silicon rectifiers (Fig. 6-3) are also very popular. A silicon unit is usually much smaller than a selenium unit. Connections are usually soldered directly to selenium rectifiers; however, silicon units may be plugged into a holder (Fig. 6-3A) or soldered in the circuit (Fig. 6-3B). Others are enclosed in containers (Fig. 6-4) which can be plugged into conventional tube sockets. Units of this type are designed to directly replace tubes.

The symbol adopted for power rectifiers is given at A in Fig. 6-5. In some instances, part of the symbol will not be shaded, as shown at B and C, or the entire symbol may be left unshaded, as shown at D. Symbols E and F are rarely used.

Courtesy Sarkes Tarzian Inc.

(A) Low-voltage.   (B) 132-volt AC.

Fig. 6-2. Selenium bridge rectifiers.

(A) Plug-in.

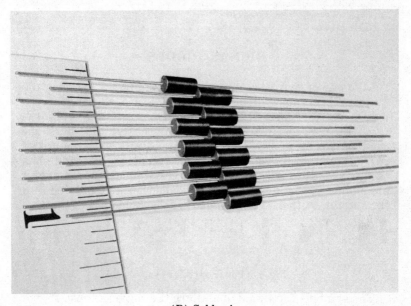

(B) Solder-in.

Courtesy Sarkes Tarzian Inc.

Fig. 6-3. Silicon rectifiers.

The bar portion in symbol A corresponds to the cathode of a vacuum tube. That is, electrons flow from it toward the arrowhead. This bar portion will sometimes be labeled with a "+" sign or the letters CATH. The same markings may be stamped on the unit itself.

Letter Codes

There is much disagreement among manufacturers about which letters to use in designating power rectifiers. Consequently, the letters *M, CR, SE, X, Y, E,* and *REC,* among others, may be encountered.

Fig. 6-4. A silicon rectifier designed to plug into a tube socket.

Courtesy Sarkes Tarzian Inc.

SIGNAL DIODES

Like power rectifiers, signal or crystal diodes perform the same function as a diode tube. The difference between the power rectifier and the signal diode, however, is in the function each performs in a circuit. Power rectifiers are used in power-supply circuits to handle large amounts of current. Signal diodes are used in signal circuits and thus they pass only small values of current. Typical signal diodes are shown in Fig. 6-6. Some have leads that are soldered into the circuits; others are plugged into a holder.

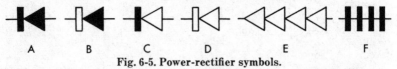

A   B   C   D   E   F

Fig. 6-5. Power-rectifier symbols.

The symbols for signal diodes are the same as those shown at A, B, C, and D in Fig. 6-5 for power rectifiers. Sometimes the symbol may be enclosed in a circle. Symbols E and F, however, are never used for crystal units. Like power

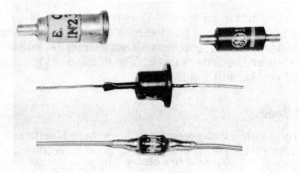

Fig. 6-6. Crystal diodes.

72

rectifiers, a "+" sign or the letters CATH are often placed near the bar portion of the symbols. Either marking may also appear on the end of the unit itself, although a colored dot or ring or some other identification is often placed there instead.

Letter Codes

Like the power rectifier, many letters are used to designate signal diodes. Some of those used are *D*, *E*, *SC*, *CR*, *XD*, *X*, and *Y*.

TRANSISTORS

In 1948, Drs. William Shockley, John Bordeen, and Walter H. Brattain of Bell Telephone Laboratories announced their development of the first transistor. Since that time, the transistor has revolutionized the electronics industry. It can be used in practically every application that a tube can be

Courtesy Philco Corp.

Fig. 6-7. A composite group of transistors.

and in some it can't—but, as was once prophesied, has not replaced tubes. They are still better suited for certain applications.

The principal advantages of the transistor over a tube are: (1) it is much smaller; hence, equipment can be made much more compact; (2) its power requirements are much lower, so large power supplies are not needed; in fact, a small flashlight cell will operate a transistor for a long time; (3) it has no heater; this further simplifies the power supply and reduces ventilation problems; and (4) it has a longer life expectancy and is less fragile.

The word "transistor" is a broad term applied to the entire field of those semiconductor devices which have three or more terminals. Fig. 6-7 shows some of the many sizes and shapes available. Each has its own particular application where it performs the same function as a vacuum tube—amplifying, mixing, oscillating, and switching, to name a few.

Transistor Construction

In function, the transistor corresponds roughly to the triode vacuum tube. Fig. 6-8 shows the construction of a typical transistor. It consists of a slab of semiconductor material to which connections are made at three points. Notice that the material at the points where two of the connections are made is labeled P-type and the remainder of the slab is labeled N-type. The adding of certain impurities to the semiconductor will alter its electrical properties. If, as a result, the material contains an excess of electrons, it is

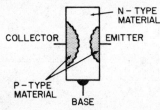

Fig. 6-8. Elementary construction of a transistor.

called N-type; if it has a deficiency, it is called P-type. Notice in Fig. 6-8 that the two areas of P-type material are separated by an area of N-type. A view of a typical transistor with the cover removed is given in Fig. 6-9. Connection to each of the different areas of the semiconductor slab is taken out to leads at the bottom. This shows a PNP-type silicon transistor, and to give you an idea of its size, the cap is ap-

Fig. 6-9. An enlarged view of a transistor with cover removed.

proximately three-tenths of an inch in diameter—only slightly larger than the eraser on the end of a pencil! When the proper voltages are applied, electrons will flow through the unit, much as they do through a vacuum tube.

Since the unit in Fig. 6-8 consists of two areas of P-type material separated by an area of N-type material, it is called a PNP transistor. This order can be reversed during the manufacturing process, so that the two areas on the outside are N-type materials and the area in the middle is a P-type. Now it is an NPN transistor.

The names of the three transistor elements are also given in Fig. 6-8. The emitter corresponds roughly to the cathode of a vacuum tube; the base, to the grid; and the collector, to the plate. However, electrons do not flow through the two types of transistors in the same direction. In the NPN type they flow from the emitter to the base and collector, whereas in the PNP type they flow from the collector and base to the emitter. Likewise, the voltages which must be applied to the collectors of the two types differ. The base of an NPN transistor must be more positive than the emitter, whereas for a PNP it must be more negative. In either instance, however, the difference between the voltages at the base and emitter will be only a few tenths of a volt.

Transistor Symbols

The symbols for an NPN transistor are given in Fig. 6-10. Notice that the arrowhead may be located at the point where the diagonal intersects the circle, as in A, or placed along the line as in B. The element with the arrowhead denotes the emitter, and the bar portion of the symbol, the base. The remaining element is the collector. The letters E, B, and C identify the elements. The emitter is shown at the top of symbol C. Even when the different elements are repositioned, the emitter is always the element with the arrowhead. The symbols at D and E are seldom encountered.

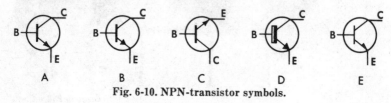

Fig. 6-10. NPN-transistor symbols.

Fig. 6-11 shows the symbols for a PNP transistor. The only difference is in the direction of the arrowhead. In the NPN transistor symbol it points *away* from the base, while for a PNP it points *toward* the base. In other words, it will always point in the direction *opposite* the flow of electrons.

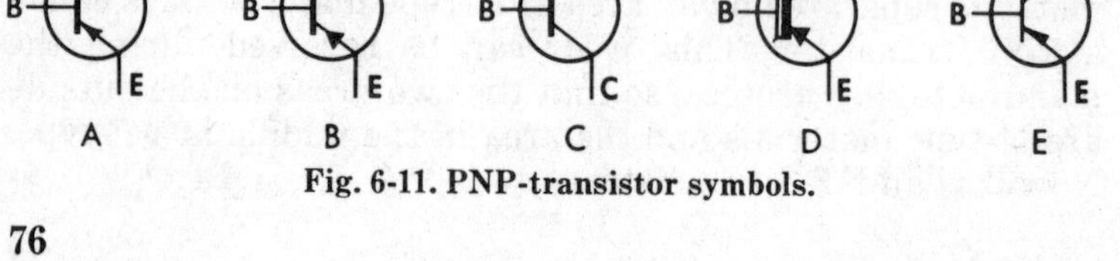

Fig. 6-11. PNP-transistor symbols.

76

(In transistor terminology this is called the direction of *hole* flow.) As with tube symbols, the circle denoting the protective covering is sometimes omitted, but this is not recommended.

Code Letters

Fewer letters are used to denote transistors of the various manufacturers than for other members of the semiconductor family. Nevertheless, the letters *Q*, *X*, *V*, *T*, and *TR* are presently employed.

OTHER SEMICONDUCTORS

There are many other types of semiconductors in use today. Some are not presently being used in consumer equipment, but no doubt you will encounter several of them as you examine various circuits. Only the more common will be discussed here.

Zener Diode

The zener diode is much like the power or signal diodes discussed previously. Its characteristics are very similar to those of power or signal diodes. Recall that a diode allows current to flow in only one direction. In the reverse direction, the diode has a high resistance. However, if a voltage higher than that at which the diode is designed to operate is applied in this direction, the diode will break down and current will flow. A normal diode may be damaged under these conditions; the zener diode is designed to operate in this manner.

Fig. 6-12. Zener-diode symbols.

In operation, the zener diode serves as a voltage regulator; that is, when the voltage exceeds a given amount, the zener diode conducts, limiting the voltage to the desired value. Fig. 6-12 shows the symbols used to denote a zener diode. Those at A and C are probably the most popular. Any of the symbols can have the circle as at A, B, E, F, and G or without as at C and D. The zener diode is also known as a backward diode, breakdown diode, avalanche diode, and voltage-regulator diode.

Silicon Controlled Rectifier

The silicon controlled rectifier (SCR), also called a *thyristor*, is actually like two transistors in construction. In operation, it is similar to the thyraton discussed in Chapter 5. The symbols used to represent an SCR are very similar to those for the diode, as shown in Fig. 6-13. In operation,

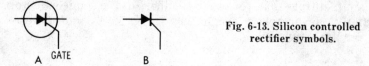

A GATE   B

Fig. 6-13. Silicon controlled rectifier symbols.

the diode will not conduct until a "trigger" current is applied to the added connection, called the gate. Silicon controlled rectifiers are used mostly in AC control applications. They are presently widely used in lighting control and power tools.

Tunnel Diode

In the normal semiconductor, it takes a certain amount of time for the current carriers to move through the unit. In the tunnel diode, however, they appear to move at the speed of light—according to Einstein's theory, the ultimate speed in the universe. At the same time, a tunnel diode is capable of amplifying—a function not normally obtained in a two-element device. Explanation of the tunnel diode is beyond the scope of this book. Tunnel diodes can be used in many types of circuits where usually only a transistor or

A   B   C   D   E

Fig. 6-14. Tunnel-diode symbols.

tube can be used. Temperature extremes and nuclear radiation have little effect on them. Fig. 6-14 shows the most common symbols used to depict a tunnel diode on schematics. As with other semiconductor symbols, the circle may or may not be used.

Capacitive Diode

Also called a varactor, *Varicap*, reactance diode, or parametric diode, the capacitive diode actually functions as a capacitor in the circuit. The symbols for this device are

78

given here instead of in Chapter 3 because most of the symbols used to depict it (Fig. 6-15) resemble those for the semiconductor diode. Recall that a semiconductor diode consists of a layer of P- and a layer of N-type material. When these two materials are joined, a layer forms at the junction which serves as an insulator. This condition is the same as for a capacitor—two conductors separated by an insulator. In the normal diode, steps are taken to minimize this capacitance.

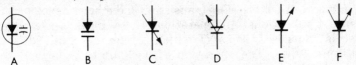

Fig. 6-15. Capacitive-diode symbols.

In the capacitive diode the capacitance is emphasized. The capacitance of a capacitive diode will vary, depending on the voltage across the diode. Thus, by varying the voltage, the capacitance varies, and a circuit can be "tuned." The greatest use of varactors has been in high-frequency applications, but they can be used in any application where a variable capacitor is called for. The limiting factor is the small degree of change in the capacitance of a capacitive diode, but recent developments indicate that this range can be increased.

Photodiodes

The semiconductor diode is a very versatile device. There seems to be no end to the uses to which it can be put by simply varying the construction and composition. Silicon diodes are also sensitive to light. In some applications they function as a resistor whose value varies according to the amount of light striking it. In this use, they are usually called light-dependent resistors. Symbols for this use were given in Fig. 2-13.

Fig. 6-16. Solar-cell symbols.

In addition, a voltage can be generated when light strikes the diode. In this application it is called a solar cell. Fig. 6-16 shows symbols used to depict the solar cell. The symbols at A, B, and C resemble the diode symbol with the arrows, letter *L*, or Greek *lambda* (λ) signifying that it is light-sensitive. The symbol at D more nearly represents a battery (to be discussed in a later chapter). As with other diode symbols, the circle enclosing the symbol may or may not be employed, but it is recommended.

Other Transistors

Several other types of transistors have been developed to serve applications. In operation, these units serve many special purposes, some of which cannot be obtained with vacuum tubes. The operation of such units is beyond the scope of this book, but Fig. 6-17 gives the symbols for several "special" transistors. The symbol at A is for an N-type unijunction transistor, which essentially has two bases and an emitter but no collector. The symbol at B is for a P-type unijunction transistor. Other names for this device are double-base diode and filamentary diode.

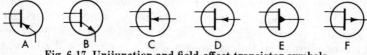

Fig. 6-17. Unijunction and field-effect transistor symbols.

The symbols at C and D in Fig. 6-17 are for an N-type–base field-effect transistor, while those at E and F are for P-type units. The field-effect transistor resembles a vacuum tube in its operation. Other semiconductors are essentially "current-operated" devices. That is, the electron (or hole) flow is the controlling factor. In vacuum tubes and field-effect transistors, the controlling factor is the voltage.

QUESTIONS

1. Name two semiconductor materials.
2. Why must a semiconductor be enclosed in a vacuum?
3. What are the two principal types of transistors?
4. What are the three elements of a transistor?
5. What code letters are used to identify transistors?
6. Draw the symbol for a power rectifier.
7. Draw the symbol for a crystal diode.
8. Draw the symbol for an NPN transistor and label the various elements.
9. Draw the symbol for a PNP transistor and label the various elements.
10. Name an important application of zener diodes.

CHAPTER 7

Switches and Relays

When a circuit is closed, a complete path is provided over which electrons can flow. Conversely, when open no path exists and hence the circuit is inoperative. Some means must be provided to open or close many of the circuits in electronic equipment. Each of the devices discussed in this chapter will perform this switching function.

SPST SWITCHES

The simplest switch is the knife switch illustrated in Fig. 7-1. When the arm moves down, it engages the clips at the end and completes the circuit to which it is connected. Such

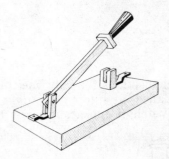

Fig. 7-1. A single-pole, single-throw knife switch.

a device is called a *single-pole, single-throw* switch (abbreviated SPST). It can make connections for only one line, and at only one point. The symbols for SPST switches are given in Fig. 7-2. All look alike except B, differing only in the arrowheads (which indicate the movable contact) and the small circles (which indicate the connection points).

Other types of construction can be used for the SPST switch, such as the familiar on-off switch for controlling our

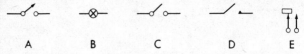

A   B   C   D   E

Fig. 7-2. Single-pole, single-throw switch symbols.

house lighting. The toggle switch, slide switch, and radio or TV on-off switch (which is activated by rotating or pulling and pushing a shaft), are all SPST units and are identified by the symbols in Fig. 7-2.

SPDT SWITCHES

The knife switch shown in Fig. 7-3 can be used to connect the center terminal to either outside terminal. It still makes

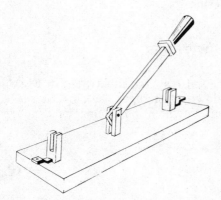

Fig. 7-3. A SPDT knife switch.

connections for only one line at a time, but to either point. Called a *single-pole, double-throw* (abbreviated SPDT) switch, it appears in many forms—toggle, slide, rotary, and

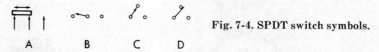

A   B   C   D

Fig. 7-4. SPDT switch symbols.

pushbutton, to name a few. The symbols for the SPDT switch (Fig. 7-4) are the same as those of the SPST except for the added connection.

DOUBLE-POLE SWITCHES

To control two separate circuits with a single switch, a double-pole unit is needed. It comprises two sections, each like the single-pole type shown previously, that are mechanically but not electrically connected. For instance, a *double-pole,*

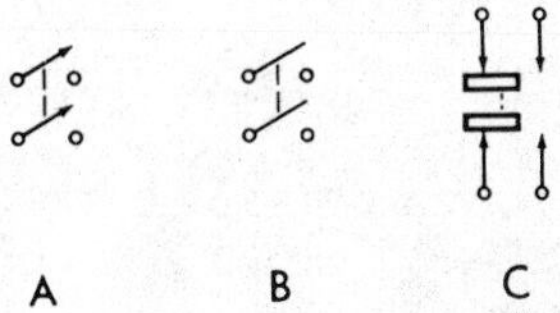

Fig. 7-5. DPST switch symbols.

A   B   C

single-throw (DPST) knife switch consists of two blades, each of which can be connected to one set of terminals. The two blades are connected, or ganged, together (by an insulating material) so that when one is moved, the other automatically follows. Fig. 7-5 shows the symbols used to denote DPST switches. The dashed line indicates that the two arms are mechanically but not electrically connected.

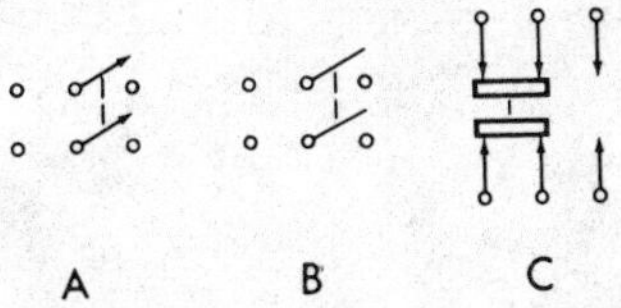

Fig. 7-6. DPDT switch symbols.

A   B   C

By adding another set of terminals to the two-bladed knife switch so that the two mechanically-connected blades make contact in either of two positions, it becomes a *double-pole double-throw* (DPDT). Fig. 7-6 shows the symbols for this type.

WAFER SWITCHES

The wafer switch shown in Fig. 7-7 is very popular for making connections to more than one point. Fig. 7-8 shows the symbols for one type. Here, the center terminal can be connected to any one of the six points around it. Often the wafer is constructed as shown in Fig. 7-9. One contact around the edge is longer so that it always makes connection with the circular ring in the center. Notice that one point on the ring extends out farther than the rest. As the switch is rotated, this point will be connected to each contact, one after another, around the outside. This, then, is actually a *single-pole, 12-throw* switch. Fig. 7-10 shows the most common symbol for it. The arrows extending from the small circles represent the contacts around the outside. The longest arrow is the longest contact. The ring is deliberately drawn so that it does not touch the arrowheads except at the long contact

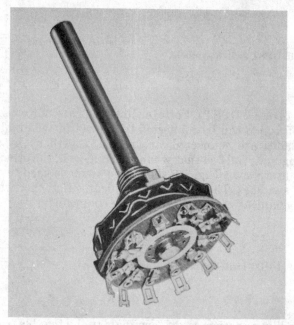

Fig. 7-7. A typical wafer switch.

and at the point of extension on the ring. As the switch is rotated, this extension contacts each arrowhead in turn. The symbol is usually pictured as being viewed from the shaft end, and the terminals are numbered clockwise, as shown in Fig. 7-10. If the wafer is being pictured from the rear, the numbers will be numbered counterclockwise, of course.

 Fig. 7-8. A single-pole, 6-position switch symbol.

A single-section wafer switch can be used when two or more circuits must be switched in and out at the same time. By making some points wider on the rotating ring, certain connections can be made between them and the stationary

84

contacts. The ring may also be broken instead of solid so that one half will serve some of the stationary contacts, and the other half the remainder. For instance, symbol A in Fig. 7-11 shows a switch in which terminals 2 and 3 are connected

Fig. 7-9. A typical wafer.

Courtesy of Centralab, Electronics Division of Globe-Union, Inc.

to terminal 5, and terminals 7 and 9 to terminal 11. The arrow at the center indicates the direction the center portion moves when the switch is rotated. Rotating the switch one position will connect terminals 3 and 4 to terminal 5, and

Fig. 7-10. A single-pole, 12-position wafer-switch symbol.

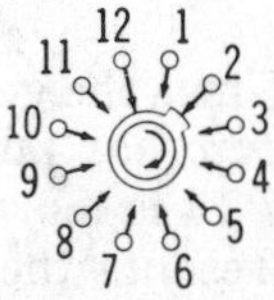

terminals 8 and 10 to terminal 11. Any number of connections can be made by such switches, each depending on the construction of the shorting ring. Two other possibilities are shown in symbols B and C.

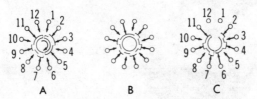

Fig. 7-11. Wafer-switch symbols.

Another method of showing a wafer switch, especially for TV tuners, is shown in Fig. 7-12. Here the switch is laid out horizontally. The bar below the row of arrowheads repre-

85

sents the inner shorting ring (which for illustrative purposes has been straightened out and broken). The jagged lines at the ends of the bar signify the broken bar. In the actual switch, the two ends are connected at this point. As the switch is rotated, the bar moves along and makes connections to the various contacts. The principal advantage of depicting the switch in this manner is that coils, which are usually connected across the various contacts, can be shown more easily.

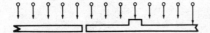

Fig. 7-12. Another method of representing a wafer switch.

Several wafer sections are often connected to a single shaft. Thus, rotating the shaft will change the connections at each section. While most of the wafer switches shown in this chapter have 12 positions, many have from 18 to 24 or more. The symbols used by some companies will vary slightly. For example, the numbers representing the terminals may be placed within the circles. Nevertheless, all symbols will be very similar to the ones shown here.

PUSH-BUTTON SWITCHES

Sometimes the general switch symbol in Fig. 7-2 is utilized for the familiar push-button switch of Fig. 7-13. Symbol A in Fig. 7-14 is more widely used, however. The vertical portion represents the button; when pushed, it moves the bar

Fig. 7-13. A push-button switch.

down to make connection across the contacts, represented by the two circles. The same switch is also shown by symbol B. Here, the arrowheads represent the contacts. Both symbols A and B represent a normally open switch. If the switch is normally closed, pushing the button will open the circuit. Symbols C and D denote this type of switch.

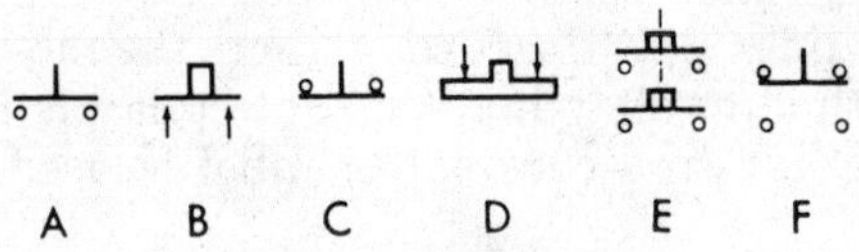

A   B   C   D   E   F

Fig. 7-14. Push-button switch symbols.

A push-button switch can also be of the double-pole variety, as shown by symbol E. Here, pushing the button closes two circuits. Symbol F represents a switch which opens one circuit and closes another when the button is pushed.

Code Letters

Switches may be designated by several different letters. The more common are S, SW, M, and E. In addition, the letters WS are sometimes used to indicate a wafer switch.

RELAYS

All the switches discussed previously were actuated by either rotating or sliding a knob, pushing a button, or some other mechanical movement. A relay is an automatic switch, which may or may not require a physical action to be activated. For instance, a relay could be connected into a photoelectric-cell circuit. When light falls on the cell, more current will flow through the tube and a relay in its plate circuit will close.

A typical relay consists of a coil of wire wound around an iron core, and two contacts. The relay becomes energized as current flows through the coil and causes its core to act as an electromagnet. One of the contacts, being movable, is attracted by this electromagnet, and in moving toward it, touches the other (stationary) contact, completing the circuit. When current through the coil decreases below a certain amount, a spring returns the contact to its original position. Just as there are many types of switches, there are also relays of many types and shapes to fit a multitude of applications. A few of them are pictured in Fig. 7-15.

The symbol for a simple relay is given at A in Fig. 7-16. The bar at the top of the symbol is the movable contact, and the arm with the arrowhead is the stationary one. The relay coil is represented by a wire wrapped around a rectangle (representing the core). The dashed line (sometimes omitted) signifies that the core attracts the movable element. Another method of showing the same relay is by symbol B; here, the regular iron-core coil symbol is used to represent the relay coil.

Courtesy Ohmite Mfg. Co.

Fig. 7-15. Various types of relays.

The relays in symbols A and B are both single-pole, single-throw units. All types of relays are available, however. For example, symbol C shows a single-pole, double-throw unit. The movable contact completes the circuit to the upper stationary contact. This is called the de-energized position (no current flowing through the coil). When current does flow, the movable contact is pulled down, opening the upper circuit and closing the lower one.

To simplify circuit layout, the connections to the relay are sometimes brought out different sides, as shown in D. The circuit between the two contacts in this relay is normally closed. When energized, the movable contact is pulled down and opens the circuit. Sometimes the letters *NC* (for normally closed) or *NO* (for normally open) are placed beside the contacts on the schematic to signify the de-energized position.

A single relay coil may operate more than one movable arm at the same time. Symbol E depicts a two-section relay. The top part is a single-pole, single-throw section which is normally closed. The bottom part is a single-pole, double-throw unit which is normally connected to the upper contact. A somewhat different way of representing a relay is given at F.

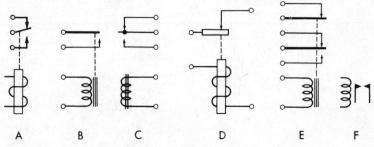

Fig. 7-16. Relay symbols.

There are innumerable possibilities in the types of relays, but their operation is obvious from examining the contacts. Just remember that the relay is normally shown in its de-energized position, and that energizing the relay will cause the position of the bar to move toward the coil.

The most common letters for designating relays on schematic diagrams are *K*, *RE*, *RL*, *M*, and *E*.

QUESTIONS

1. What is the basic purpose of a switch?
2. What type of switch is most commonly used as the on-off switch for a radio?
3. What type of switch does the abbreviation SPDT indicate?
4. What is the purpose of the switch in Question 3?
5. What is a relay?
6. What does a dashed line between two points on a switch symbol indicate?
7. What is the purpose of the coil in a relay?
8. What are three of the code letters used to designate switches on schematics?
9. Draw the symbol for a double-pole, double-throw switch.
10. Draw the symbol for a single-pole, double-throw relay.

CHAPTER 8

Miscellaneous Components

Nearly all the components discussed in the previous chapters will be found in any one piece of electronic equipment. In most cases, more than one of each will be included. Even so, it is exceedingly rare that such equipment can be constructed from those components alone. Instead, many other items are necessary for its operation.

Don't think that because they have been classified as "miscellaneous," the components to be discussed in this chapter are less important. This is not true. For instance, what good would a radio be without a speaker? The reason for the miscellaneous classification is that *all* the items in this chapter are not necessarily found in *every* piece of equipment.

ANTENNAS

No piece of transmitting or receiving equipment is complete without an antenna. At the transmitter, it is the final unit in the system. From it, the electromagnetic waves are "sent out" through the air to the receiver. Here, the antenna is the first unit in the system, intercepting these electromagnetic waves and conveying or coupling them to the input. Sometimes the antenna is not an integral part of the equipment, but is mounted externally (on a roof, tower, etc.). In such a case the antenna symbol may not be included on the schematic, but only the terminals where it is to be connected (see next chapter).

Symbols

Fig. 8-1 shows the symbols commonly employed for antennas. Symbols A, B, and C generally designate external antennas.

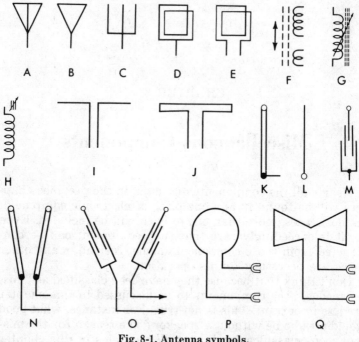

Fig. 8-1. Antenna symbols.

Two methods of depicting the familiar loop antenna are shown by D and E. (A loop antenna is a coiled length of wire usually fastened flat against the back of the cabinet.) Other versions of this symbol may be employed, but all will resemble this general layout. Another type of built-in antenna may use either symbol D, E, F, G, or H. This is called a *ferrite-loop* antenna (Fig. 8-2). It is actually a coil of wire wound around a ferrite core. Besides having the advantage of being very sensitive to weak signals, it is also tunable. The length of wire attached to the unit may be stretched out for additional pickup. Notice that symbols F, G, and H are the same as those for a coil, which this type of antenna actually is.

Methods of indicating TV antennas are shown by symbols I through O in Fig. 8-1. Symbol I is often used for any type, but actually represents a dipole—the basic TV antenna.

Symbol J is another basic TV antenna—the folded dipole. The symbols at K, L, and M are for a monopole antenna (the single telescoping rod built into portable TV receivers). The symbols at N and O are for the same type of antenna, except with two telescoping rods. A built-in UHF antenna is represented by the symbols at P and Q.

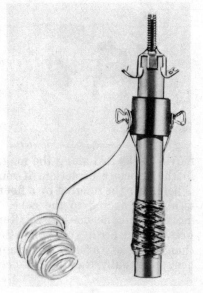

Fig. 8-2. A ferrite-loop antenna.

Courtesy Stancor Electronics, Inc.

Code Letters

Since all antennas—no matter how constructed—are so similar in function to a coil, many manufacturers use the letter *L* to designate them. Others prefer *I* or *M*.

SPEAKERS

The speaker is the final link in the chain of stages in a radio receiver or amplifier and in the sound system of a TV receiver. Its purpose is to convert the electrical signals, which vary in step with the sound to be reproduced, into the actual sounds.

A cutaway view showing the construction details of a typical 4-inch speaker is given in Fig. 8-3. The speaker operates as follows: The signal voltage is impressed across the voice-coil terminals and is carried from there to the voice coil by leads. Thus, a current which varies in step with the signal flows through the voice coil. A permanent magnet inside it interacts with the magnetic lines of force set up by the current. When the current flows in one direction, the voice coil

Fig. 8-3. Cutaway view of a speaker.

Courtesy Quam Nichols Co.

moves backward along the magnet; and when current flows in the opposite direction, it moves forward. The voice coil is held over the magnet by a fiber disc called the *spider*, which is also connected to the cone. Therefore, as the voice coil moves, the cone does also, alternately expanding and compressing the air in front of it. Sound waves are nothing more than cycles of rarefied and compressed air, so the sound we hear is actually the disturbances produced by the cone.

Fig. 8-4. A coaxial speaker.

Courtesy Jensen Manufacturing Co.

Another type, called a coaxial speaker, is pictured in Fig. 8-4. Actually, it is two speakers in one. The large cone around the outside reproduces the low frequencies, and the small cone in the center the high frequencies.

In another type of speaker, the permanent magnet is replaced by an electromagnet consisting of a coil of wire, called the field, wound around a soft-iron core. When a direct cur-

94

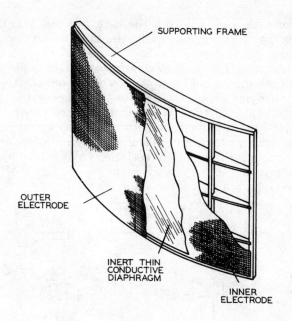

(A) Construction.

Courtesy of Pickering & Company, Inc.

(B) Photograph.

Fig. 8-5. An electrostatic speaker.

rent flows through the coil, the core becomes magnetized, making the operation essentially the same as for the permanent-magnet speaker.

The construction of an *electrostatic* speaker is pictured in Fig. 8-5. As shown in Fig. 8-5A, it is composed of a thin plastic diaphragm, plus an electrode on either side, through which sound can pass. It is sometimes referred to as a capacitor-type speaker because of its construction. The two electrodes act as the plates of a capacitor, and when an audio signal is applied to them, its variations move the diaphragm accordingly and thereby produce the sound. Fig. 8-5B shows a commercial unit.

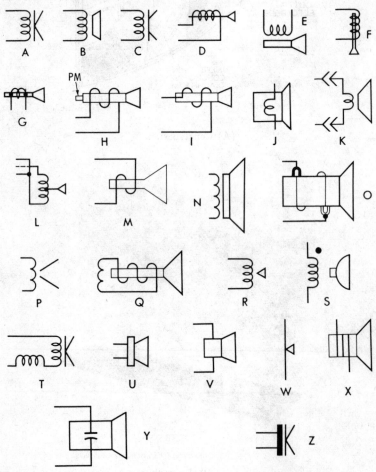

Fig. 8-6. Speaker symbols.

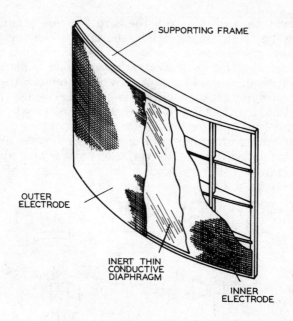

SUPPORTING FRAME

OUTER
ELECTRODE

INERT THIN
CONDUCTIVE
DIAPHRAGM

INNER
ELECTRODE

(A) Construction.

(B) Photograph.

Fig. 8-5. An electrostatic speaker.

rent flows through the coil, the core becomes magnetized, making the operation essentially the same as for the permanent-magnet speaker.

The construction of an *electrostatic* speaker is pictured in Fig. 8-5. As shown in Fig. 8-5A, it is composed of a thin plastic diaphragm, plus an electrode on either side, through which sound can pass. It is sometimes referred to as a capacitor-type speaker because of its construction. The two electrodes act as the plates of a capacitor, and when an audio signal is applied to them, its variations move the diaphragm accordingly and thereby produce the sound. Fig. 8-5B shows a commercial unit.

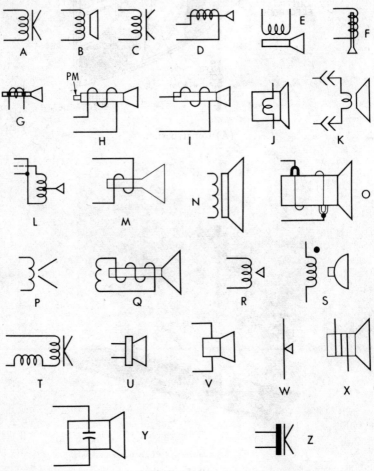

Fig. 8-6. Speaker symbols.

Symbols

Many different symbols are used for speakers, as shown in Fig. 8-6. Symbols A through S all show the voice coil and cone of a PM speaker. For an electromagnetic speaker, another winding called a *hum-bucking coil* will usually be added, as shown in symbol T. Its purpose is to cancel out any hum introduced by the speaker field. The field winding may be shown as a separate iron-core coil near the speaker symbol or elsewhere on the schematic.

Symbols L through X designate no particular speaker; they can be used for all types. Two symbols for indicating electrostatic speakers are given at Y and Z. There may be other variations, but all will resemble those for a PM speaker.

Sometimes the symbol for a single speaker is also used to depict the coaxial type of Fig. 8-4. At other times, two speaker symbols enclosed in a dashed-line box may be employed. Other minor variations of the symbols shown in Fig. 8-6 may be encountered; however, they will usually resemble those shown in this illustration.

Code Letters

The letters *S*, *SP*, *SPK*, *LS*, *E*, and *M* are most commonly employed by the various companies to designate speakers.

FUSES

Unless some protection is provided, a short or other malfunction could destroy an entire piece of electronic equipment. This protection is provided by fuses, some typical types being shown in Fig. 8-7. When a circuit draws too much current, the metal strip or wire inside the fuse melts, interrupting the excessive flow.

There are many types of fuses. The one at A in Fig. 8-7 is a 20-amp fast-acting type—the instant the current exceeds its rating, it will open. The slow-blow type B does not open if a momentary surge of current higher than its rating flows through it, unless the surge is prolonged.

The fuse at C is enclosed in a steatite instead of glass covering. The one at D has a rating of only .01 amp and is used to protect a meter circuit, while the one at E is designed to withstand the high vibration encountered in aircraft. Other similar fuses have leads extending from their ends so they can be soldered directly into the circuit.

All the fuses in Fig. 8-7 are inserted into holders (Fig. 8-8; the item at the lower left is a fuse puller). Fig. 8-9 shows another type of fuse and its mounting. It is only

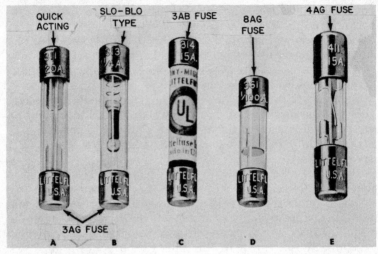

QUICK ACTING SLO-BLO TYPE 3AB FUSE 8AG FUSE 4AG FUSE

3AG FUSE

A   B   C   D   E

Fig. 8-7. Various sizes of fuses.

Fig. 8-8. Various types of fuse holders and a fuse puller.

0.27 × 0.25 inch. The two leads fit into the matching holes in the holder and the cap is inserted over it.

Another type of fuse and holder is shown in Fig. 8-10. Here, the fuse is twisted to lock it in place in the holder. The length of the fuse and the width of the locking tabs differ according to rating. Thus, the wrong size of fuse cannot be inserted.

98

Courtesy Bussman Mfg. Div., McGraw-Edison Co.
Fig. 8-9. A miniature plug-in fuse.

Fuse Symbols

Symbols A and B in Fig. 8-11 are used by nearly every company to designate fuses. The only difference between the two is the addition of the circle in B to denote the terminals. The symbol at C is sometimes used for a special type of fuse in which a chemical is used in place of a wire. Symbols D

Courtesy Bussman Mfg. Div., McGraw-Edison Co.
Fig. 8-10. An N-type fuse and its holder.

through H are all occasionally encountered. Symbol F is actually a drawing of the fuse, and G is a combination of A and F.

Code Letters

Most companies designate fuses by the letter *F* on their schematics, although some prefer *M* or *E*. The rating usually appears on the schematic, alongside the fuse symbol and, if a slow-blow type, this fact will usually be noted, too.

CIRCUIT BREAKERS

The circuit breaker performs the same function as a fuse, but does not destroy itself in case of an overload. It merely opens two contacts, which are restored by pressing a button.

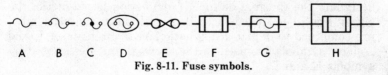

Fig. 8-11. Fuse symbols.

The circuit breakers in modern home electrical systems are a familiar application of this principle. Other circuit breakers are made for the small value of current in TV receivers or similar equipment.

There are two basic principles of operation for circuit breakers. In the thermal type, the current heats a metal strip which bends enough to open the contacts when the current reaches a predetermined value. When the strip cools, the contacts can be closed again by pushing the reset button. In the other type, an electromagnet (formed by a coil of wire) has sufficient strength to attract one of the contacts and open the circuit when the current reaches the prescribed limit. Again, pushing the reset button closes the circuit. (However, it will open again if the overload still exists.) Some units combine the thermal and magnetic principles.

Symbols

Several symbols are used to represent circuit breakers. The ones at A, B, C, and D in Fig. 8-12 denote both thermal and magnetic types. Symbol A is sometimes altered to show the method of operation. For example, adding a slant line to the curved portion of the symbol as in E indicates a switch-type breaker. Symbol F indicates a push-pull unit, and symbol G a push-push breaker.

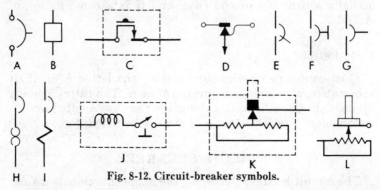

Fig. 8-12. Circuit-breaker symbols.

The symbol for a thermal unit is given by H in Fig. 8-12. It is a combination of symbol A and two partial circles which designate the thermal action. If the action is magnetic, the zigzag line in I is used instead. A coil and a switch symbol are combined to depict a magnetic circuit breaker in J, and resistor symbols are used in the thermal unit designated by symbols K and L.

100

Code Letters

The most common code letters for circuit breakers are *CB*, *M*, *RC*, and *E*. Sometimes the letter *F* is used, however. This is a carryover from the fuse which the breaker replaces.

LAMPS

Two types of lamps are generally employed for lighting the dials and other indicators in practically all types of electronic equipment. The first is a regular incandescent type similar to the common flashlight bulb. The other obtains its lighting properties from a rare gas, such as neon.

Incandescent Lamps

The incandescent lamp is always used where illumination, rather than a warning signal, is needed. For example, many radio and TV dials have lamps behind them to make the markings visible. In other equipment a lamp may be placed behind a jeweled bead which glows to indicate that the unit

Fig. 8-13. Incandescent dial-lamp symbols.

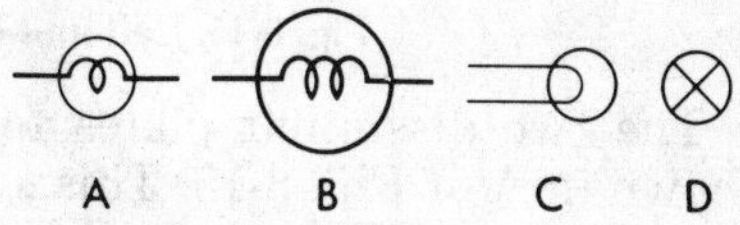

A   B   C   D

is on. The symbols for dial lamps are given in Fig. 8-13. The circle depicts the glass envelope of the bulb; and the portion inside represents the wire, which gives off light when heated. The letters *I, B, F, M, P, PL, V,* and *E* are used by the various companies to depict an incandescent lamp.

Neon Lamps

The neon lamp gives off only a soft red glow when lit. Its widest application, therefore, is as an indicator. It consists of two plates, called electrodes, separated by the neon gas.

A   B   C   D   E   F   G

Fig. 8-14. Neon-lamp symbols.

The symbols for neon lamps (Fig. 8-14) all depict these two electrodes. The only difference is in the manner in which they are drawn and in the dot (which always symbolizes gas)

101

inside the envelope. Symbol E is for AC lamps only, and symbol F is its DC counterpart. The same code letters designate neon as well as incandescent lamps. *I*, *M*, and *B* are the most common, however. Sometimes the letters *NE* (for neon) are also employed.

BATTERIES

Batteries power many types of portable equipment. Essentially, all batteries consist of two dissimilar materials in a solution—either plates immersed in an acid, as in the automobile storage battery; or a carbon rod and a zinc container with a solid material between them, as in a flashlight cell. (A cell, often incorrectly called a battery, is the basic unit. A battery is two or more cells used together to provide the desired voltage or current. For example, a 12.6-volt storage battery contains six cells, each supplying 2.1 volts.)

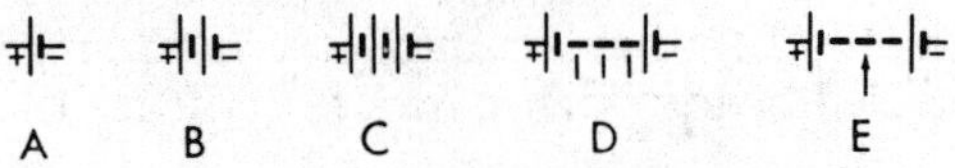

Fig. 8-15. Cell and battery symbols.

The two dissimilar plates form the symbol for a cell, as shown in A of Fig. 8-15. This symbol is practically universal in acceptance. The shorter bar represents the negative, and the longer bar the positive, plate. Often the "+" and "−" signs are also included on the symbol, as shown; sometimes only the plus sign is included.

Sets of bars are added to depict multicell units, as shown in B and C—but don't be misled into believing the number of pairs of bars always conforms to the actual number of cells in the battery. Sometimes they do, but usually no more than four or five sets of bars are employed, no matter how many cells they represent. Symbol D denotes a battery with taps at various points, and E a battery with a variable tap. Such symbols are rather rare, however.

Letters *B*, *BT*, *E*, and *M* are the most common for identifying batteries on schematics.

CRYSTALS

Crystals are made from materials, such as quartz, which have the unique property of generating a voltage when pressure is applied to them. Conversely, when an alternating volt-

102

age is applied, they will bend or twist in synchronism with the variation. By cutting a crystal at various angles and to different dimensions, and by making electrical connections to it with a metal plate on each side (called a holder), the crystal can be made to oscillate or vibrate at what is called its *resonant frequency*.

Once a crystal starts oscillating, only a very small force is required at the same frequency to obtain large-amplitude oscillations. These oscillations of alternating voltage are often connected to the grid circuit of a crystal-oscillator stage. Since a crystal will oscillate at only one frequency (determined by its dimensions), the frequency of the crystal-oscillator stage will remain constant.

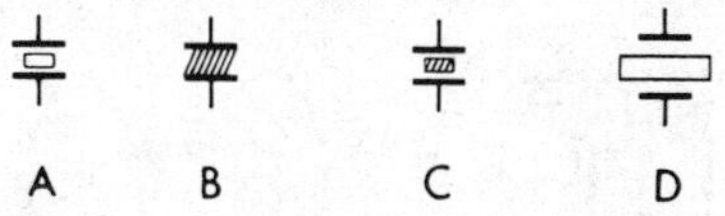

Fig. 8-16. Crystal symbols.

A   B   C   D

The symbols for a crystal in Fig. 8-16 illustrate its physical construction. The two bars represent the holder, and the rectangle or slanted lines, the crystal element.

The letters Q, Y, M, and X are used by various companies to identify crystals on their schematics.

VIBRATORS

In battery-operated equipment, the vacuum tubes sometimes require a much higher voltage than the battery can provide. The DC voltage cannot be stepped up by a transformer. Although not used much in present-day equipment, a vibrator (Fig. 8-17) formerly was commonly used to change the steady DC to a pulsating DC, which can then be

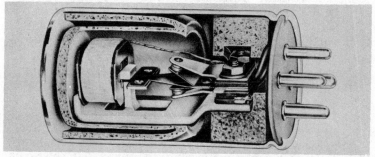

Courtesy P. R. Mallory & Co., Inc.

Fig. 8-17. Cutaway view of a typical vibrator.

stepped up by a transformer. The applied voltage is then rectified to change it back to a steady DC. When the battery voltage is applied to the vibrator (Fig. 8-17), the coil at the top electromagnetically attracts the reed (the T-shaped element directly below it). When the reed moves, one pair of contacts near the bottom closes, shorting out the voltage to the coil at the top. With no force to hold it, the reed springs back, closing the other set of contacts and allowing current to flow through them. This action opens the first set of contacts, re-energizing the coil, and the cycle is repeated. This is how the vibrator contacts continuously interrupt the flow of current through the primary winding of an accompanying power transformer.

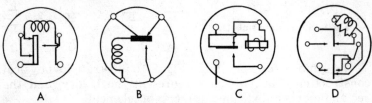

Fig. 8-18. Vibrator symbols.

The symbols for vibrators are merely representations of the connections within the unit. Fig. 8-18 shows some examples. About the only difference in the symbols is that sometimes the pins (indicated by circles) are shown within the outer circumference in the same arrangement as they appear on the actual vibrator, and at other times are placed around the outside. Symbols A and B show these two methods, the conventional coil symbol being used in both. Another method is employed in C. Here, the contacts are represented by the arrowheads, and the vibrating reed by the heavy bar. The connections within different vibrators may vary considerably. Only four of the many combinations are illustrated in Fig. 8-18. The only difference among the other types will be in the number of contacts and in the connection of the components within the unit.

Vibrators are identified by the letters V, E, G, VB, and M on the schematics of most companies.

MICROPHONES

Sound waves, as they exist, cannot be boosted in strength. Nor can they be mixed directly with the signal at a radio station and transmitted over the airwaves. True, a megaphone can direct the sound to a certain point, but the total power contained will not be increased.

Before sound waves can be amplified, they must be changed into an electrical signal. This signal can then be put to a number of uses—it can be boosted in strength by an amplifier and converted back to sound by a speaker, mixed with the radio or TV station signal (called "modulating"), applied to the head of a tape recorder to record the signal on tape, etc.

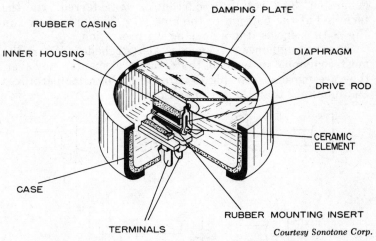

Fig. 8-19. Construction details of a ceramic microphone.

A microphone changes sound waves into a varying electrical signal. Thus, its purpose is just the opposite from that of the speaker discussed earlier in this chapter. A speaker, however, will work as a microphone. Most intercom systems use a conventional speaker which, by proper switching, also acts as a microphone.

One type of microphone employs a coil which moves in a magnetic field and thereby converts sound into electrical waves. As the sound waves strike the diaphragm, the coil movement induces a voltage in the coil. Such microphones are called *dynamic* or *moving-coil* types.

Several other principles are used for microphones. The carbon type consists of a brass cup filled with compressed carbon granules. A diaphragm connected to the cup is moved back and forth by the sound waves. The movement changes the pressure on the granules and hence the resistance of the carbon to the flow of current through it. Another microphone operates on the capacitor principle—the sound waves move a plate back and forth with respect to a fixed plate and thereby change the capacitance.

Fig. 8-19 shows the construction of a *ceramic* microphone. Here the sound enters the louvered plate at the top and strikes the diaphragm, moving it back and forth. The ceramic element (barium titanate), connected to the diaphragm by the drive rod, exhibits properties similar to those of the crystal discussed earlier in this chapter. That is, as the pressure of the sound waves bends the ceramic unit, a voltage is generated. The resulting current is transferred, via the terminal at the bottom, to the amplifier. The unit shown in Fig. 8-19 is enclosed in a housing for protection.

Some microphones employ crystals (Rochelle salts are the most common) instead of the ceramic elements. However, they are more susceptible to damage by high temperatures and humidity than the ceramic units.

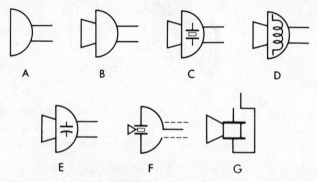

Fig. 8-20. Microphone symbols.

The most common symbols for a microphone are shown in A and B of Fig. 8-20. When these symbols are used, the type (crystal, magnetic, etc.), is usually designated by a note beside the symbol. Symbols C, D, and E represent crystal (ceramic), dynamic, and capacitor microphones, respectively. In F and G are shown two methods of combining a standard microphone symbol with the symbol showing the type (in this example, crystal or ceramic). Similar versions are sometimes used for other types of microphones. The microphone symbol is often omitted from schematics because it usually is not an integral part of the unit. Instead, only the terminals to which it is connected are shown.

The letters *M*, *MIC*, or *E* are the most popular for microphones. Often, no code letter is used. Instead, the type of microphone is written out beside the symbol.

TRANSDUCERS

The microphones described in the preceding are designed to pick up sounds that we can hear and convert them to electrical waves. Other devices are very similar, but are designed to respond to sounds we cannot hear. A common example of this application is the use of ultrasonic sounds for remote control of a television receiver. In this application the unit is called a transducer, or ultrasonic microphone. (Actually the term "transducer" describes any device for transferring the flow of energy from one or more systems to one or more other systems. Thus, a speaker is also a transducer; a sonar

Fig. 8-21. Ultrasonic-transducer symbols.

pickup is another transducer. The application of the term "transducer" to ultrasonics is quite common, however.) Fig. 8-21 shows some of the symbols used to depict ultrasonic transducers. As with microphones, many materials are used for construction. The type may be designated by a note beside the symbol.

HEADSETS AND EARPHONES

Like the speakers discussed previously, the headset or earphones convert a varying voltage into sound. Some of them are constructed much like a speaker. Usually, two coils are placed over two pole pieces which are permanent magnets. These pole pieces attract a metal diaphragm suspended over them. As the current through the coils varies, the magnetic field it sets up is alternately added to and subtracted from the field of the permanent magnets. This changing field moves the diaphragm back and forth in step with the voltage.

Other types of headsets have crystal or ceramic elements. They operate like the microphone discussed previously, except in reverse. That is, a varying voltage is applied to the crystal or ceramic slab, which in turn moves the diaphragm back and forth.

The two basic symbols for headsets and earphones are given by A and B in Fig. 8-22. Symbol C is for a double headset. Additional circles are sometimes placed inside the symbol, as shown by D. Symbols E and F, a combination of those in Fig. 8-20 and A in Fig. 8-22, designate a handset (a combination microphone and earphone) used in telephone and some intercom systems.

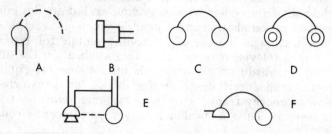

Fig. 8-22. Earphone, headphone, and handset symbols.

PHONO PICKUPS

The phono cartridge converts into electrical signals the vibrations produced by the variations in a record groove. It bears a close resemblance to the microphone, where the variations in sound waves are converted into electrical signals. Many symbols have been devised for depicting the phono cartridge. Since some are monaural and others are for stereo, and since some have one needle and others two,

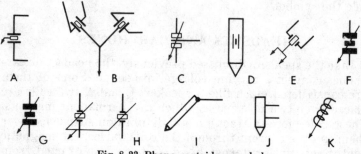

Fig. 8-23. Phono-cartridge symbols.

differences in indicating them are inevitable. Symbols A and B in Fig. 8-23 are similar except that B represents a stereo cartridge. Two crystal elements are shown, but only one needle. Other ways of indicating crystal or ceramic cartridges are given by C through H. The symbols at G and H are for stereo cartridges, while a magnetic cartridge is symbolized by K. Symbol D can also be made to signify a magnetic pickup by substituting a coil symbol for the crystal symbol on its body. Usually, when a pickup is not an integral part of the actual circuit, no symbol is used; instead, a socket into which it connects is shown on the schematic.

In place of the code letter, an identifying note is often placed beside the symbol for a pickup. When employed, the letters M, P, and PU are the most popular.

TAPE HEADS

In a magnetic tape recorder the heads perform three functions. The first function is essentially the same as that of the phono pickup. The head converts the variations in the recording to an electrical signal which corresponds to the sound that has been recorded. This electrical signal is then amplified before it is applied to a speaker, where the electrical signal is converted to sound. The difference between a tape head and a phono pickup is that on a phonograph record, variations are cut in the groove to correspond to the signal. In a tape recorder, a varying magnetic field is applied to the tape which holds this magnetic pattern. As the tape passes the head, a signal is developed in the head circuit which varies in step with the signal originally used to magnetize the tape.

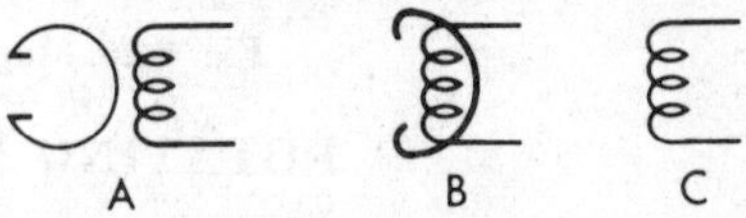

Fig. 8-24. Magnetic-head symbols.

A   B   C

The second function provided by magnetic heads is to record the signal on the tape. Essentially this is the reverse of the pickup. Here the signal is applied to the head. As the tape passes the head a varying magnetic field is set up in the tape corresponding to this signal. Often the same head is used for recording and playback, and the connections to the head are changed by a switching arrangement.

The third function of heads is erasing. Magnetic tape can be used over and over. Once a pattern is recorded on the tape, it will remain on the tape until it is erased by bringing it in contact with a magnetic field. This magnetic field can be DC or a high-frequency AC, but the AC is more common. Most tape recorders have a head which contacts the tape just ahead of the recording head. Called the erase head, it removes any signal on the tape just before the new signal is recorded. During playback, no signal is applied to this head so the signal will not be removed. Fig. 8-24 shows the symbols for tape-recording heads. The ones at A and B show a combination of a coil and a circular element. This is similar to the actual construction of a magnetic head, as shown in the photo of Fig. 8-25. A coil is sometimes used by itself to show a magnetic head. Usually a note will be placed by the symbol to explain its function. The symbols at A and B in Fig. 8-24 will usually have an *R* (record), *P* (playback), or *E* (erase) inside the circular portion. If the head is used for both recording and playback, an *R/P* will be used.

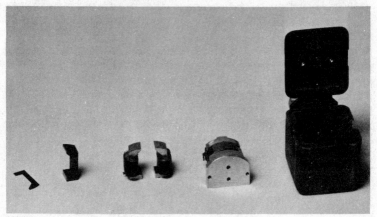

Fig. 8-25. Magnetic heads.

ROTATING MACHINES

Although not classed as electronic equipment, motors, generators, dynamotors, etc., are sometimes included on schematic diagrams. Phonographs, tape recorders, and fans are examples of equipment using motors.

Motors

The basic symbol for a motor is an *M*, the letters *MOT*, or the word *MOTOR* placed either alongside or inside a circle, as shown by A in Fig. 8-26.

Where it is desirable to show the connections to the motor, symbols B and C may be used. In symbol B, the field coil is in series with the armature, while symbol C shows it in parallel. (The coil symbol depicts the field, and the circle the armature.) Two methods of showing phonograph motors are illustrated by symbols D and E. Some other representative methods are depicted in F through J. In each instance, the symbol is drawn to conform with the motor connections.

110

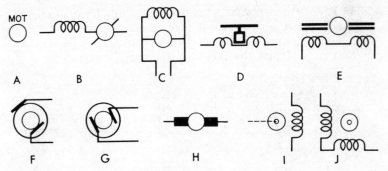

Fig. 8-26. Motor symbols.

Generators

In general, symbols for generators are the same as for motors, except the letter *G*, the letters *GEN*, or the word *GENERATOR* will be used, of course.

Dynamotors

Dynamotors are sometimes used in communications equipment to step up a low DC voltage. They are made up of a DC motor and generator with a single field winding and a common armature, but separate commutators. The symbols resemble those for motors and generators, as shown by the two representative symbols in Fig. 8-27.

Fig. 8-27. Dynamotor symbols.

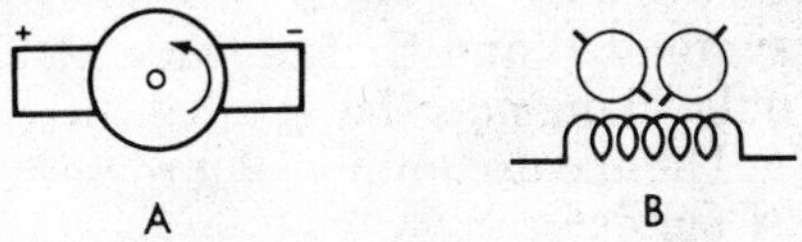

A   B

SOLENOIDS

A solenoid is an electrical device which provides some mechanical action, such as closing a valve or sounding a door chime, when a voltage source is connected to it (by pushing a button, for example).

A solenoid consists of a coil surrounding a movable iron core attached to a spring. When current flows through the coil, the core is either attracted farther into or repelled partially from it. The movement of the core actuates the device to which it is connected. When the current through the coil ceases, the spring returns the core to its original position.

As you have probably guessed, the symbol for a solenoid is like that for a coil with a core, as shown by A and B in Fig. 8-28. An arrow will sometimes be added, as shown in C, D, and E, to depict the fact that the core is movable.

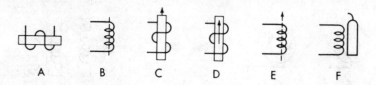

Fig. 8-28. Solenoid symbols.

METERS

Meters are sometimes included in electronic equipment so that operating conditions or other information can be monitored. They are often depicted by symbol A in Fig. 8-29, accompanied by identifying letters inside or alongside it. An

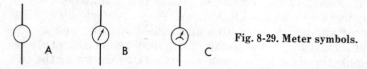

Fig. 8-29. Meter symbols.

arrow may be added to indicate the pointer, as shown by symbols B and C. The same identifying letters are used, but only alongside the symbol, of course.

The most common abbreviations for identifying the type of meter are:

A—ammeter
AH—ampere-hour meter
CRO—oscilloscope
D—demand meter
DB—decibel meter
F—frequency meter
G—galvanometer
I—indicating meter
M—integrating meter
MA—microammeter
NM—noise meter
OHM—ohmmeter

PH—phasemeter
PI—position indicator
PF—power-factor meter
REC—recording meter
S—synchroscope
TLM—telemeter
V—voltmeter
VA—volt-ammeter
VI—volume indicator
VU—volume-unit meter
W—wattmeter
WH—watt-hour meter

OTHER SYMBOLS

Up to this point we have discussed practically every component used in electronic equipment. Fig. 8-30 illustrates the symbols used for some items which will occasionally be found, particularly in specialized equipment. Symbol A is for a spark plate used in automobile radios. It consists of a

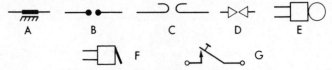

Fig. 8-30. Miscellaneous component symbols.

metal plate placed alongside the chassis and separated by an insulating material. Three methods of depicting lightning arresters are shown by B, C, and D. Symbol E is for a bell, while F depicts a buzzer. Symbol G is for a telegraph key.

Fig. 8-31. Amplifier symbols.

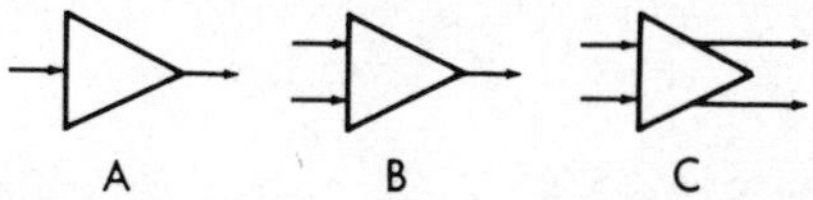

A manufacturer will sometimes want to show a drawing of a large installation, but not every circuit component. On this type of diagram, an entire amplifier is indicated by a triangle, as shown by A in Fig. 8-31. For more complicated circuits, two inputs and a single output will be shown as in B, or two inputs and two outputs as in C.

QUESTIONS

1. What is the purpose of a speaker?
2. What circuit element destroys itself when it performs its intended purpose?
3. What are the two types of lamps used in entertainment-type equipment?
4. What is the difference between a cell and a battery?
5. Name three types of microphones.
6. Draw the symbol for a headset.
7. Draw the symbol for a voltmeter.
8. Draw the symbol for a crystal.
9. Draw a battery symbol and indicate the polarity.
10. What does this symbol indicate?

CHAPTER 9

Connecting the Components

All components are useless unless they can be interconnected. There are many ways to do this. One—the printed circuit—was a contributing factor in the development of the "personal-sized" transistor radio discussed earlier.

WIRES

The most widely known method of connection, of course, is by means of a wire. It can be an actual wire run between two points, or the wire (more commonly called lead) of a component. Nevertheless, the two are indicated in the same way on the schematic.

As you probably know, a line denotes a wire or a component lead. There are three methods of showing whether two leads are connected or not. The first is illustrated by A in Fig. 9-1. The vertical line at the left intersects the horizontal line, indicating in this system that they are connected. Now notice that the lead at the right has a half-circle at the crossover point. The half-circle means that this wire (called a jumper) bypasses the horizontal line.

In the system at B, the dot placed at the point where the left vertical line crosses the horizontal denotes that the two lines are connected. Conversely, no dot at the intersection of the right vertical and the horizontal lines indicates no connection.

These two systems can be confusing if you don't know off hand which one is being used. In A, two crossed lines indicate a connection, whereas in B, they indicate just the opposite.

For this reason, it is always best to carefully study the schematic first. If jumpers are used at some places, you know that the crossed lines indicate a connection. Dots at the point where some lines cross alert you to the fact that lines crossing without dots do not connect. The system at C in Fig. 9-1,

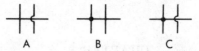

Fig. 9-1. Three methods of showing connecting and nonconnecting leads.

actually a combination of the two previous systems, eliminates any chance of confusion. The dot (at the left) indicates that the two lines connect. To be on the safe side, the jumper (at the right) is also used to indicate no connection.

GROUND AND CHASSIS SYMBOLS

Three other symbols often seen on schematics are given in Fig. 9-2. Those at A, B, C, and D are referred to as ground symbols. Actually, the term "ground" is a carryover from

Fig. 9-2. Ground and chassis symbols.

the early days of radio, when the receiver was literally connected to the earth (ground). The term "earth" is used in British terminology to describe this point. Today, the more popular symbol A designates a common-return point for all circuits. Otherwise, a line would have to be drawn to all of them. Imagine how cluttered up the schematic would be! All points exhibiting this symbol are considered connected.

Often, the ground symbol signifies the chassis of the equipment. Instead of the various points being connected by a wire, they are merely connected to the metal chassis. This is true except in AC/DC equipment, where doing so would necessitate connecting the chassis to one side of the power line. This would make the chassis "hot"; anyone touching it would receive a shock. In this type of circuit, the chassis is designated by the symbol at E in Fig. 9-2.

Sometimes, particularly in high-fidelity equipment, a heavy copper conductor called a "bus bar" will be positioned near several stages and connected to ground. All circuits are then returned to ground through it instead of directly to the chassis. The advantage of such an arrangement is reduced hum. The bus bar may be indicated on the schematic by an extra heavy line.

OTHER METHODS OF DENOTING CONNECTIONS

Companies are constantly striving to make their schematics easier to read. A long, winding line is most difficult to follow around a schematic when the connections are remote and widely separated. Eliminating as many lines as possible is one way to simplify a schematic. For example, instead of drawing them from the voltage sources in a power supply to their destinations, an arrangement like that in A of Fig. 9-3 can be used. Each source is indicated by a dot and labeled with the voltage available at that point. Then, all other points connected to this source are indicated by an arrow accompanied by the available voltage, as shown at B.

Fig. 9-3. A common method of showing connections to voltage sources.

Instead of the arrow in Fig. 9-3, a circle of the same diameter as the dots in the power supply is sometimes substituted. Coded letters such as A, B, and C occasionally are used instead of listing the actual voltage.

Some companies employ triangles, squares, diamonds, and other geometric designs to signify connection between two points. Usually, the source is indicated by a solid-colored symbol, and the points connected to it by the outline of that symbol.

Similar methods have been adopted for designating connections between points other than voltage sources. Usually,

117

letters are employed—all points labeled with the same letter are assumed to be connected.

Sometimes two points are interconnected by a cable (several wires bundled together), usually designated by symbol A in Fig. 9-4. The ring surrounding all wires represents the outer covering of the cable, and may be placed at each end or in the center. If the cable is shielded, a ground symbol may

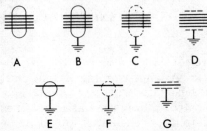

Fig. 9-4. Cable and shielded lead symbols.

be added to the symbol at A, as shown at B. Also, a dashed circle may be used, or a dashed line above and below the lines representing the wires, as shown at C and D. A ground symbol will be connected to the dashed lines, as shown at C and D. The same systems are also used for designating a single shielded lead, as shown by symbols E, F, and G. The dashed lines at G may extend the entire length of the cable or wire, or for only a short distance as shown here.

CONNECTING DEVICES

Sockets, plugs, and jacks are only a few of the many types of connectors. All have one thing in common—a convenient means for connecting and disconnecting two points. Imagine the problem every housewife would face if her toaster had no plug and she had to fasten the leads to the wall outlet every morning!

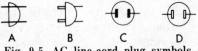

Fig. 9-5. AC line-cord plug symbols.

The symbol for connectors is usually an actual drawing. Symbols A, B, and C in Fig. 9-5 are good examples; A and B are side views and C is an end view. Symbol D is for a socket. The symbol for a pronged unit (plug) is solid-colored, and

118

hollow for the open unit (the socket). The same system is used for most plug-and-socket combinations. Fig. 9-6 depicts only a few of them. In each instance, the symbols show the actual arrangement of the plug pins or socket openings.

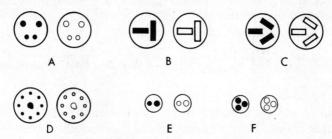

Fig. 9-6. Plug and socket symbols.

Fig. 9-7 illustrates five methods of showing connections for single leads. Symbols A and B are for the familiar phono-type plug and socket found on the rear of many radio and TV receivers. Symbols C, D, and E all depict simple one-wire connectors. The arrow head in symbol C is the plug and the remainder is the socket. Symbols D and E use the same solid and hollow representation explained before.

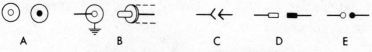

Fig. 9-7. Single-wire connector symbols.

If the socket and plug contain so many connections that it would be difficult to show leads from all the pins, a different method is sometimes used. The various points may be arranged in a row and each pin and socket terminal numbered, as shown in Fig. 9-8. A separate drawing showing the pin

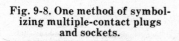

Fig. 9-8. One method of symbolizing multiple-contact plugs and sockets.

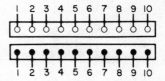

numbering and arrangement is usually included on the schematic also. Instead of the arrangement of Fig. 9-8, individual connections may be shown, as in C, D, and E of Fig. 9-7. Each is then labeled with the plug or socket number, followed by a dash and a number denoting the pin. Most of the time, plugs

119

and sockets are not identified by code letters. When they are, the letters *P* or *PL* (for plug) and *S* or *SK* (for socket), or *X* and *M* are the most popular.

Terminals for the antenna, speaker, etc., connections must also be shown on schematics. Fig. 9-9 shows some of the more common designations.

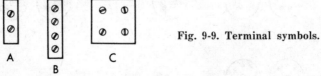

Fig. 9-9. Terminal symbols.

Jacks and their matching plugs (Fig. 9-10) are also used in many types of equipment, usually to make or break connections as the plug is inserted. Fig. 9-11 shows some typical symbols for jacks of this type. (The arrow shown with symbol A indicates the direction in which the plug is inserted, but is not a part of the symbol.) When inserted, the tip of the plug is connected to the upper terminal in symbol A. In B, the plug strikes the V-shaped portion connected to the upper terminal, forcing it up and disconnecting it from the center terminal. As before, contact is made between the upper terminal and the plug. Sometimes the plug will cause a contact to be made instead of broken, as in symbol C. Many other combinations are possible, as shown by symbols D through G.

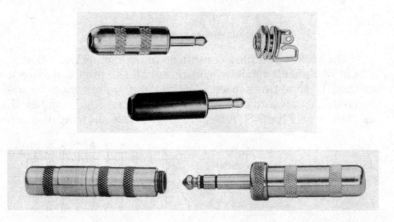

Courtesy Switchcraft, Inc.

Fig. 9-10. Typical plugs and jacks.

The symbols showing two V-shaped elements indicate a jack with two separate connectors contacting two points of

120

the plug. Both points are normally insulated from each other. For example, one may be on the tip of the plug, and the second on another portion called the ring.

The cross-hatched pattern of the symbol at F signifies that the two points to which they are attached are joined mechanically but not electrically. All the symbols in Fig. 9-11 show a bar or rectangle at the front depicting that portion of the jack (called the sleeve) which extends out of the chassis, and into which the plug is inserted. This area will sometimes be shown as a heavy solid bar.

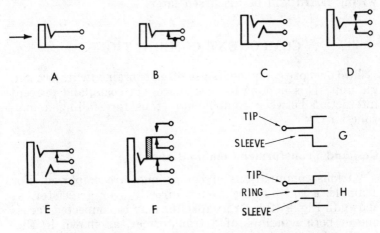

Fig. 9-11. Symbols for various types of jacks and plugs.

The symbols at G and H in Fig. 9-11 are for plugs. The one at G is for a two-conductor plug, and the one at H is for a three-conductor plug.

Like sockets, jacks and plugs are usually not assigned code letters. But if they are, the letter *J* is the most popular for jacks, and *P* or *PL* for plugs, although *X* and *M* may sometimes be employed.

PRINTED CIRCUITS

In many types of modern electronic equipment, the wiring has been replaced by a printed circuit. Appropriately named, a printed-circuit board comprises a phenolic base onto which the conductors are embossed with a conductive paint. Its biggest advantage is that tedious hand wiring is no longer necessary. Instead, the circuits can be mass produced by machines, a process which is not only quicker but also more reliable. Compactness in equipment design is another virtue of printed circuitry.

On the debit side, a printed-circuit board is easily broken, often beyond repair. Nevertheless, its use has mushroomed in the past decade. The connections made by the printed wiring are shown in exactly the same manner as with hand wiring. If only part of the circuit is printed, that portion may be outlined by a dashed line and identified as such. Ways of identifying the different points of the printed-wiring board will be discussed later.

COMPONENT COMBINATIONS

Two or more components are often contained within a single unit. This is done to save space, cut costs, and prevent interaction between components (thus forestalling a malfunction).

Coil and Transformer Combinations

Various combinations of components are employed. For example, a coil may be wound directly over a resistor, as shown in Fig. 9-12A. Or a capacitor may be connected across one or both windings of a transformer, as shown in Fig. 9-12B. The schematic representations for these two units, as well as other popular combinations, are given in Fig. 9-13.

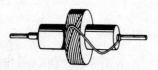

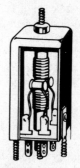

Courtesy Stancor Electronics, Inc.

(A) A resistor and coil.

(B) A transformer with capacitors connected across each winding.

Fig. 9-12. Component combinations.

122

The symbols may be enclosed in a dashed-line box which signifies that all components within it are part of an individual combination unit. Notice the ground symbol connected to the box in C—it indicates that the components within the box are shielded from the rest of the circuit. That is, stray magnetic fields cannot enter or leave the box. This shielding is provided by a metal cover (or *can* as it is more commonly called) which touches the chassis and is thus grounded to it.

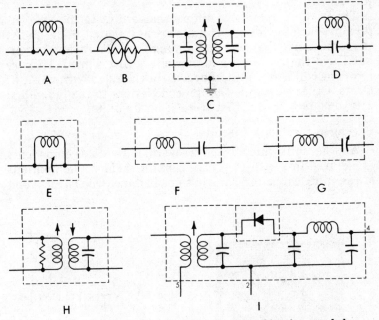

Fig. 9-13. Various coil and transformer combination symbols.

Some of the other combinations are also given in Fig. 9-13. The units represented by symbols D, E, F, and G all contain a coil and capacitor. Symbol D has a fixed capacitor connected directly across a coil. In symbol E, the coil is also in parallel but with a variable capacitor. The coils and capacitors in F and G are connected in *series*.

The transformer in symbol H has a resistor connected across one winding and a capacitor across the other. Many other similar combinations are possible. Symbol I represents a transformer, three capacitors, a coil, and a crystal diode—all occupying a single can. Notice that the dashed lines extend all the way around the crystal diode, signifying that the diode itself is entirely enclosed by a separate can. Usually the diode

123

is mounted in two clips on top of the regular can, over which a metal cover is placed to shield the diode.

This same dashed-line symbol with the ground connected to it is used in many ways to designate a shield. As mentioned previously, when drawn around a lead or group of leads, it represents a shielded wire or cable. At other times, it may be placed around a tube symbol on a schematic to denote that a shield is placed over the tube after it has been inserted into its socket.

The various companies differ considerably in the code letters by which the foregoing units are designated. Some assign the same L or T that they do for a regular coil or transformer, but leave the resistors and capacitors unassigned. If more than one coil is included, they are subclassified with an A, B, C, etc. Other companies assign code letters to the individual components just as if they were separate units.

Packaged Electronic Circuits

Another unit which includes several individual components is pictured in Fig. 9-14. These contain various combinations of resistors, capacitors, and in some instances, coils, all bound

Fig. 9-14. A packaged electronic circuit.

to a base plate and sealed with a protective coating. Such units are extremely resistant to moisture, temperature, and shock. Fig. 9-15 should give you an idea of the time and space saved by using these devices. All the components on the left are contained within the single unit on the right. By using this unit, nine soldered connections are eliminated and only one-sixth of the space is required. This unit has nine external leads and contains all the components necessary for coupling between two stages of a radio receiver.

These units are usually represented schematically by using regular resistor and capacitor symbols. The combination is then enclosed within dashed lines to indicate they are contained in a single unit. Each lead is numbered at the point where it extends from the dashed lines.

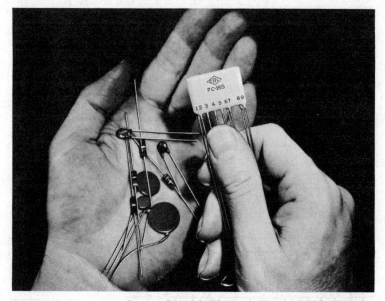

Courtesy Centralab, Electronics Division of Globe-Union Inc.

Fig. 9-15. A packaged electronic circuit and the components it replaces.

There are myriad units employing this type of construction. Each will vary only in the number of components, their connection, or their value. Fig. 9-16 A through G shows some of the available combinations.

The dashed lines around the components in the unit are sometimes omitted. Occasionally, the symbol at H in Fig. 9-16 may be used, and it may or may not be enclosed within dashed lines. The internal connection is usually shown elsewhere on the schematic.

There are several methods of assigning code letters to these packaged units. Some companies will assign one code letter (*A*, *E*, *K*, *M*, *N*, *X*, *PC*, *PN*, *DC*, or *RC*) to the entire unit. Others will assign the letters *R* and *C* to the unit, and designate the individual components as *A*, *B*, *C*, etc. Still others may combine the two methods, assigning a code letter and a number to the entire unit and then designating the components within the regular *R* and *C* designations.

125

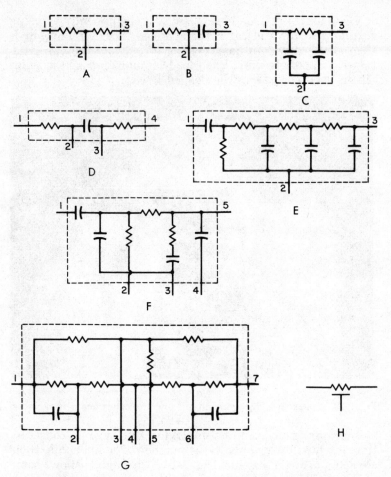

Fig. 9-16. Packaged electronic-circuit symbols.

Integrated Circuits

The latest development in the combining and miniaturization of components is being pointed out in the photo of Fig. 9-17. The integrated circuit is actually a specially constructed semiconductor device. The unit in Fig. 9-17 performs the functions which would require 26 separate conventional components (one coil, two transistors, two diodes, seven capacitors, and fourteen resistors.) Here it is housed in a conventional transistor case; it could be placed in a much smaller unit, except it would be too small for ease of handling and attaching leads.

126

Fig. 9-17. An integrated circuit installed in a television receiver.

The actual equivalent circuit of the integrated circuit may be shown on a schematic and enclosed in dashed lines, as shown in Fig. 9-18. (Notice that while the unit in Fig. 9-17 replaces 26 *conventional* components, the equivalent circuit contains many more components.) Usually, however, a triangular or rectangular symbol (Fig. 9-19) will be shown on the schematic to represent the integrated circuit. Terminals are added to these symbols to connect the various external connections. Then the equivalent circuit will usually be included elsewhere.

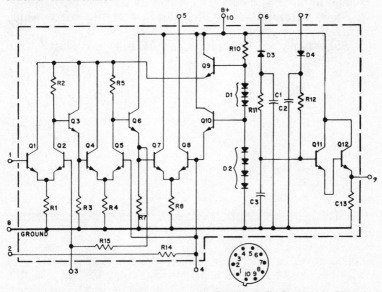

Fig. 9-18. Equivalent circuit of the integrated circuit in Fig. 9-17.

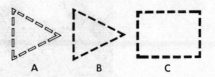

Fig. 9-19. Integrated-circuit symbols.

QUESTIONS

1. Why is it advantageous to show all voltage sources together and then indicate the points which connect to them?
2. Does a symbol which has a solid black dot depict the socket or the plug portion of the unit?
3. Are the terms "ground" and "chassis" synonymous?
4. What does a heavy line connected to ground indicate?
5. How are printed circuits shown in schematics?
6. Name two advantages of using component combinations.
7. What does a dashed line around a component (or group of components) with a ground symbol connected to it indicate?
8. What does the letter *A* or *B* following the code letter and number of a component usually indicate?
9. Show two methods of illustrating crossing wires which are not connected.
10. Show two ways of depicting an AC line-cord plug.

CHAPTER 10

Combining the Components

In the previous chapters, we have discussed practically every component used in electronic equipment and the methods of connecting them. Also, we have shown how sometimes several components are combined in a single unit. However, before any of these components can serve a useful purpose, they must be connected to form a circuit.

What is a circuit? A circuit is any combination of components connected in such a manner that it will perform its intended function. There are two general types—passive and active.

A passive circuit is one which does not contain a tube or transistor; that is, it is merely a combination of resistors, capacitors, and coils. In certain applications, such a circuit can perform many useful functions. For example, frequencies below a certain point will pass through the circuit in Fig. 10-1A and on to the following circuit. Above a certain frequency, the signals are shunted (bypassed) to ground by the capacitors. The opposite is true of the circuit in Fig. 10-1B. This is a high-pass filter. Below a certain frequency, the signals are shunted to ground through the coils; above this frequency, they are passed on to the next stage.

There are many passive circuits, or configurations as they are sometimes called, like the ones in Fig. 10-1. Each performs a definite purpose in the over-all operation of the unit.

While power must be supplied to a passive circuit, an active circuit is one which supplies power. It may be composed of batteries, a generator, or an amplifier.

To understand the operation of active circuits, in the remaining pages of this chapter we will examine some of the basic circuits and see how they operate.

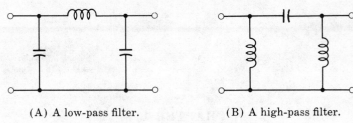

(A) A low-pass filter.   (B) A high-pass filter.

Fig. 10-1. Two passive circuits.

RECTIFIER CIRCUITS

Perhaps the simplest circuit is the rectifier shown in Fig. 10-2. Recall that in order for a diode tube to conduct, the plate must be more positive than the cathode. Then electrons will flow from the cathode to the plate. The plate (pin 5) is connected to an alternating voltage. Hence, during the periods when the plate is positive, electrons will flow from the cathode to the plate. However, these electrons must come from somewhere. They flow from ground, up through R2, then through R1 to the cathode. Since electrons flowing through a resistor produce a voltage drop across it, a voltage (which will be positive at the top) will be produced across R2. This voltage will also be present on capacitors C1 and C2.

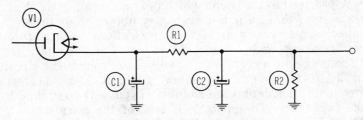

Fig. 10-2. A typical rectifier circuit.

During the period when the alternating voltage on the plate is negative, the tube will not conduct. But since the primary purpose of a capacitor is to store electrons, it will hold the charge previously placed on it and maintain the voltage relatively constant. Thus, while AC is applied to the plate, the current through R2, R1, and the tube is DC. This is the purpose of the rectifier—the AC has been converted to DC. The voltage at the output of the rectifier, called the B+ voltage, is used to power other tubes in the unit. This circuit will operate in the same way if a semiconductor rectifier is used in place of the tube in Fig. 10-2.

130

BASIC TUBE CIRCUITS

Fig. 10-3 shows the basic triode amplifier circuit. The plate of the tube is connected (through resistor R2) to the DC B+ voltage explained in the foregoing. The signal, which is AC, is applied to the left plate of capacitor C1. Since an AC signal will, in effect, pass through the capacitor, it also appears at the grid of the tube. As explained in Chapter 5, this signal will be amplified by the tube and appear at the plate. Here, capacitor C2 couples the amplified signal on to the next tube (or stage as it is called in electronics terminology).

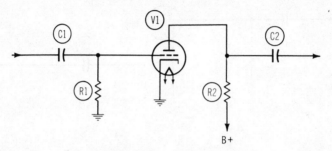

Fig. 10-3. An R-C–coupled grounded-cathode amplifier circuit.

The circuit in Fig. 10-3 is called a resistance-capacitance–coupled (R-C) circuit. A transformer-coupled circuit is given in Fig. 10-4. Its operation is similar to that of the circuit in Fig. 10-3. The transformer secondary and C1 are tuned so that only a very narrow band of frequencies will pass. Therefore, only the desired frequencies are coupled to the grid of the tube. The amplified signal appears at the plate and is coupled via T2 (which is tuned by C2 to the desired frequency) to the next stage.

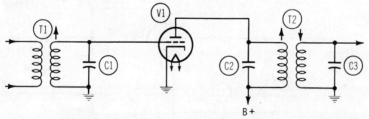

Fig. 10-4. A transformer-coupled amplifier circuit.

Another type of circuit is given in Fig. 10-5. Here the signal is coupled to the grid of the tube via C1—the same as in Fig. 10-3. However, here the similarity ends. Notice that the plate is connected directly to the B+ voltage source, so the signal will be bypassed to ground by the filter capacitors in the power supply. Also notice R2 and C2 connected to the cathode. In this circuit, called a *cathode follower*, the signal is developed across resistor R2 and coupled to the next stage by C2. No gain is accomplished in this circuit; in fact, there will be a slight loss. But, in certain applications the cathode follower has advantages over the amplifier circuit of Fig. 10-4.

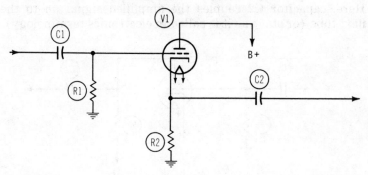

Fig. 10-5. A cathode-follower circuit.

Still another version of the triode amplifier is given in Fig. 10-6. This is called a *grounded-grid* amplifier. The signal is applied to the cathode, and the output is at the plate in this circuit. As you can see, the grid is not actually connected to ground as implied by the name. However, capacitor C1, connected between the grid and ground, serves as a bypass capacitor and removes any variations in the voltage which might occur at the grid.

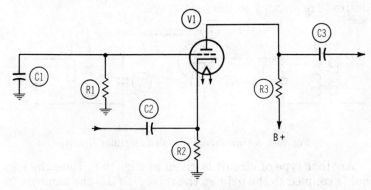

Fig. 10-6. A grounded-grid amplifier circuit.

Other Circuits

There are many variations in the basic circuits given in the foregoing. As explained in Chapter 5, often tetrode or pentode tubes are employed. Except for the added components for the screen circuit, operation is basically the same as for the triodes given here. Normally the signal is applied to the grid. The changes in the grid voltage caused by this signal increase or decrease the number of electrons which can flow through the tube from cathode to plate. Thus, the number of electrons flowing out the plate and through the plate load (i.e. the resistor or transformer winding connected to the plate) varies in step with the signal on the grid. This varying electron flow produces a varying drop across the plate load, and this drop is coupled to the next stage. Since a small change at the grid produces a much larger change at the plate, the signal is said to be amplified.

The foregoing is true no matter whether a triode, tetrode, or pentode tube is used. There are many special circuits which will generate their own signal, change the form of the applied signal, and perform many other functions. How these circuits operate is beyond the scope of this book. Suffice it to say that the same basic idea of electrons flowing from cathode to plate, and the amount of this flow being affected by the elements between the cathode and plate, still applies.

Tube Voltages

All tube voltages are measured with respect to the cathode. Often the cathode is connected to ground; at other times it is connected through a small-value resistor to ground. In the first instance, the actual voltage at the cathode is zero; in the latter, it will be a few volts positive. It makes no difference what the actual cathode voltage is—it could be -100 volts or $+100$ volts—as long as the voltage on the other elements is maintained in the proper relationship.

The grid is usually a few volts negative *with respect to the cathode*. The actual amount will vary with different tubes. Both the plate and the screen are positive with respect to the cathode. Normally this difference will be from 100 to 200 volts, but sometimes it is less and sometimes more. Usually the plate will be slightly more positive than the screen grid, but sometimes the two voltages will be the same, and in certain instances, the screen will be more positive than the plate. The suppressor grid is usually connected to ground or to the cathode; hence, at most there will be only a few volts difference between it and the cathode.

BASIC TRANSISTOR CIRCUITS

Like tubes, transistors can be connected in three different ways—the common emitter, common base, and common collector. Also, since both PNP and NPN transistors are used, the number of variations is doubled. Now let's look at each of the basic transistor circuits and see how it operates.

The Common-Emitter Circuit

A common-emitter circuit using a PNP transistor is given in Fig. 10-7A, while the same circuit with an NPN transistor is given in Fig. 10-7B. Like its vacuum-tube counterpart—the grounded-cathode amplifier—the common-emitter circuit is the most popular. First look at Fig. 10-7A. The signal is coupled via C1 to the base of transistor Q1. R1 and R2 establish the proper operating voltages on the base, and R3 establishes the operating voltage on the emitter. The amplified signal appears across R4 and is coupled to the next stage via C3.

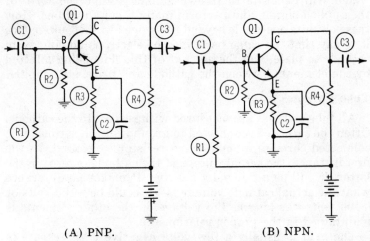

(A) PNP.   (B) NPN.

Fig. 10-7. Common-emitter circuits.

The circuit in Fig. 10-7B is the NPN version of the same circuit. Again, the signal is coupled to the transistor via C1, and the amplified version of the signal appears across R4 and is coupled via C3 to the next stage.

The only difference between the two circuits in Fig. 10-7 is the type of transistor and the way the battery is connected in the circuit. (The operating voltages will be discussed later.)

The Common-Base Circuit

The two circuits in Fig. 10-8 show the PNP and NPN versions of the common-base circuit. The input signal is coupled to the emitter of the transistor via C1. The amplified signal appears across R3 and at the collector of the transistor. Here it is coupled to the next stage via C3.

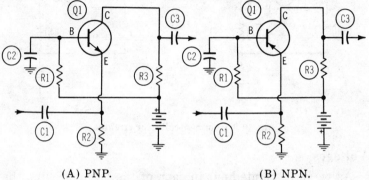

(A) PNP.   (B) NPN.
Fig. 10-8. Common-base circuits.

Resistor R1 establishes the correct operating voltage at the base. Note, however, that this resistor is bypassed by capacitor C2. Thus C2, by alternately storing and releasing electrons, removes any variations and maintains the base at a constant voltage. Since the voltage is constant as far as the signal is concerned, it is at ground potential. This is the same as for the grounded-grid tube-type amplifier discussed previously. As in Fig. 10-7, the two circuits in Fig. 10-8 are identical except for the type of transistor and the polarity of the battery.

The Common-Collector Circuit

The PNP and the NPN versions of the common-collector circuit are given in Fig. 10-9. The input signal is coupled by C1 to the base of transistor Q1, and the output signal appears across emitter resistor R3. Then it is coupled via C3 to the following stage. Resistors R1 and R2 establish the proper operating voltage at the base of the transistor. R4 performs the same function at the collector but, like the base of the previous circuit, the collector is bypassed by a capacitor (C2). Hence, as far as the signal is concerned, the collector is at ground potential. Again, the only differences in the two circuits are the transistor type and the polarity of the battery.

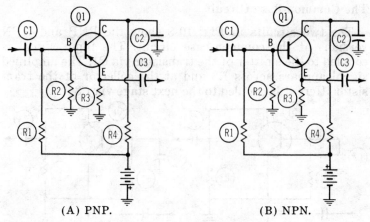

(A) PNP.   (B) NPN.

Fig. 10-9. Common-collector circuits.

Voltages

As we have pointed out in each of the basic circuits, the negative terminal of the battery is connected (through a resistor) to the collector of a PNP transistor, while for the NPN transistor the battery is reversed. Unlike a tube, in which electrons always flow in one direction (from cathode to plate), the electron flow through the two types of transistors is in opposite directions.

Electrons always flow from the negative terminal of a battery, through the circuit, to the positive terminal. In a PNP transistor electrons flow from collector to emitter; hence, the collector must be the most negative point. The base is maintained a few tenths of a volt negative with respect to the emitter. Therefore, the emitter has the most positive voltage of any of the elements.

The opposite is true of the NPN transistor. Here, the electrons must flow from the emitter to the collector. Therefore, the emitter is the most negative point. The base is a few tenths of a volt positive with respect to the emitter, and the collector is the most positive point.

SUMMARY

The circuits discussed in this chapter are the *basic* amplifier circuits. In the next chapter, we shall see how these circuits are modified for use in actual radio receivers. The basic principles outlined in this chapter apply to all of the circuits—regardless of the refinements.

136

QUESTIONS

1. What is the purpose of a rectifier?
2. What is a passive circuit?
3. In which direction do electrons flow through a diode tube when the plate is negative with respect to the cathode?
4. What are the two types of transistors?
5. Which of the basic tube circuits produces a loss?
6. In which direction do electrons flow through an NPN transistor?
7. What element of the tube is used as the reference point for all tube voltages?
8. What are the three basic transistor circuits?
9. What are the three basic tube circuits?
10. From what terminal of a battery do electrons flow?

CHAPTER 11

Reading and Interpreting Schematic Diagrams

Most schematics follow the same general arrangement. The input is normally at the upper left-hand corner, and from here, the path is usually arranged in rows from left to right and from top to bottom. Starting at the input, you can trace your way through the individual circuits as if you were reading a book. The best way to read a schematic is to analyze each stage, forming a mental image of what happens in it, and then see where its output goes. This is the input of the next "block" in the equipment. Continue through all the stages until you reach the output device (i.e., speaker, picture tube, indicator, etc.).

If this pattern is followed for any schematic, the operation of any equipment—whether it be a radio or TV receiver, transmitter, radar, or even a computer—should become apparent.

RADIO-RECEIVER SCHEMATIC ANALYSIS

The schematic of a typical five-tube AC-DC radio receiver is given in Fig. 11-1. Let's see just what information it contains.

The Signal Path

It is suggested that you refer to Fig. 11-1 as we follow the signal from tube to tube (stage to stage in electronics terminology) on its journey through the radio. The same general principles can then be applied to many other circuits.

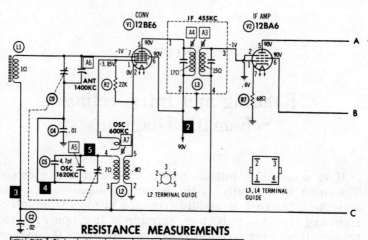

RESISTANCE MEASUREMENTS

ITEM	TUBE	Pin 1	Pin 2	Pin 3	Pin 4	Pin 5	Pin 6	Pin 7
V1	12BE6	22K	.4Ω	16Ω	29Ω	1500Ω †	1500Ω †	4.3meg
V2	12BA6	4.3meg	0Ω	29Ω	42Ω	1500Ω †	1500Ω †	68Ω
V3	12AV6	6.8meg	0Ω	16Ω	0Ω	1meg	0Ω	470K †
V4	50C5	150Ω	470K	42Ω	90Ω	470K	1500Ω †	180Ω †
V5	35W4	NC	NC	90Ω	125Ω	125Ω	120Ω	20K ⧧
ITEM	TUBE	Pin 1	Pin 2	Pin 3	Pin 4	Pin 5	Pin 6	Pin 7

⧧ READING DEPENDS ON CONDITION OF ELECTROLYTIC IN CIRCUIT
† MEASURED FROM PIN 7 OF V5
NC NO CONNECTION

Resistors are 1/2 watt or less and rated
10% or 20% unless otherwise indicated.

⊖ See parts list
1. Voltage measurements taken with vacuum tube voltmeter.
2. All controls set for normal operation, no signal applied.
3. Measured values are from socket pin or terminal to common ground.
4. All terminals viewed from bottom unless otherwise designated.
5. Numbers assigned to terminals may not be found on the unit.
6. Supply voltage maintained at rated value for voltage readings.

Fig. 11-1. Schematic of an

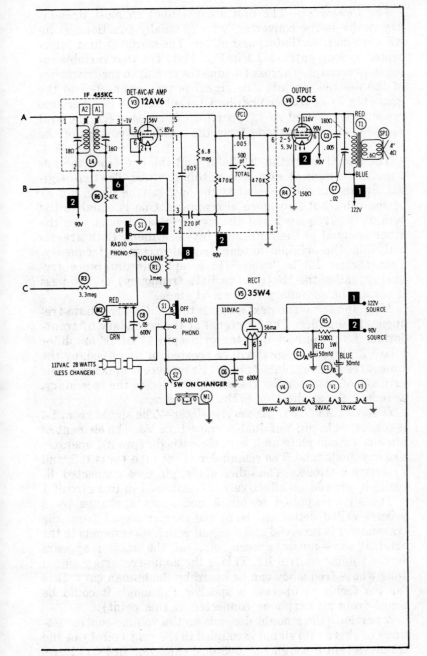

AC-DC radio with phono.

The Converter—The first stage (tube) in most present-day radios is the converter, which actually functions as an RF amplifier, oscillator, and mixer. The signal is first intercepted by loop antenna L1 in Fig. 11-1. The two variable capacitors connected across L1 tune the circuit to the frequency of the desired station. The signal is then connected to the grid (pin 7) of converter tube V1. Coil L2, the two variable capacitors (C9 and A5), capacitor C5, resistor R2, the grid (pin 1), and the cathode form the oscillator portion of the stage.

The signal from the oscillator and the one from the antenna are combined, or mixed, within the tube. The two original signals are still present at the output (the plate, pin 5) of the tube, but two more also appear. One is equal to the sum of the frequencies of the two original signals, and the other is equal to the difference between them. Both are exactly like the original antenna signal except in frequency. Transformer L3 is "tuned" to accept this difference frequency, called the IF (intermediate frequency) and to pass it across the secondary to the next stage.

IF Amplifier—The next stage is the IF (intermediate-frequency) amplifier. The IF signal at the secondary of transformer L3 is connected to the grid (pin 1) of IF amplifier tube V2. Here the signal will be boosted, or amplified, by the time it reaches the plate (pin 5). From here it appears at the primary of transformer L4, and is coupled to the secondary, as before, for application to the next stage.

Detector, AVC, and Audio Amplifier—The signal from L4 is connected to pin 5 of dual-purpose tube V3. The element at pin 5 is a diode plate and, with the cathode (pin 2), operates like any diode tube. The remainder of the tube (pins 1, 2, and 7) forms a triode. (The other diode, pin 6, is connected directly to ground, so effectively it is not used in this circuit.)

The signal applied to pin 5 undergoes a change by a process called detection. Here the carrier signal from the transmitter is removed and a signal which corresponds to the original one—music, speech, etc.—at the station appears across volume control R1. This is the audio-frequency signal (one whose frequency can be heard by the human ear). It is far too feeble to operate a speaker (although it could be heard from an earphone connected at this point).

A portion (the amount depends on the volume-control setting) of this audio signal is coupled to the grid (pin 1) of the triode section through the .005-mfd capacitor in PC1. Here, it is amplified by the tube and appears across the 470K resistor in component combination PC1, ready for coupling to the next stage.

Another voltage is also developed, at the bottom of R6. Called the AVC (automatic volume control) voltage, it varies according to the strength of the signal received at the antenna. It is applied through L3 to the IF amplifier, and through L1 to the mixer stage to change the gain, or amount of amplification. Thus, if the signal becomes stronger or weaker (say, because of atmospheric conditions), the gain of the previous stages is automatically decreased or increased accordingly, to compensate for the change.

Audio-Output Stage—The signal across the 470K resistor (in PC1) is coupled via the .005-mfd capacitor (also in PC1), to the grid (pin 2 or 5) of tube V4. Like the other stages, it amplifies the signal which appears at the plate and across transformer T1. The speaker (SP1) connected across the secondary of T1 converts the amplified signal into sound.

Power Supply—Before any of the stages discussed in the foregoing can work, the proper voltages must be applied to them. This is the purpose of the components located in the lower-right corner of the schematic (Fig. 11-1). The line cord, which is plugged into a 117-volt AC outlet, is shown at the left. The next symbol is for an AC interlock, a special type of plug-and-socket arrangement that removes the line voltage from the receiver when the back is removed. When switch S1B is moved to the radio position, it connects one side of the line to the tube.

RF bypass capacitor C6 removes any high-frequency noise that might be present on the power lines and be passed into the receiver. The tap on the rectifier-tube filament allows a dial lamp to be connected between pins 4 and 6, although not used in this receiver. The 6.3 volts between these two points is just the proper amount for the lamp. The line voltage, minus the 6.3-volt drop between pins 4 and 6, is connected to the rectifier plate (pin 5).

You will recall from the previous chapter that a diode (or any other tube) will conduct only when its plate is more positive than its cathode. The AC line voltage varies from positive to negative; hence, during the positive half-cycles the tube conducts and a pulsating DC is present at the cathode (pin 7). The two-section electrolytic capacitor (C1A and C1B) and resistor R5 smooth out these pulsations. Thus the voltage at the output is essentially DC.

The symbols connected in a row and extending from pin 3 represent the filaments of the other tubes in the radio. This arrangement, called a series string, is most popular for the smaller home radios. The sum of the voltage requirements for all tubes is the same as the applied line voltage. Hence, by connecting them across the line in this manner, no separate transformer is needed to lower the voltage to the value required for each individual tube. The disadvantage is that, like the old-fashioned Christmas-tree lights, if one burns out it opens the circuit and they all go out.

In addition to the radio, the unit in Fig. 11-1 includes a phonograph. Notice that in either the radio or phono position the shorting bar on switch S1B will connect AC power to the rectifier tube. Closing switch S2 will cause power also to be applied to the phono motor M1. Switch S1 is a two-section switch; the other portion (S1A) is located below tube V3. In the radio position the output of the detector (pin 5 of V3) is connected to the volume control through the switch. In the phono position, the converter, IF amplifier, and detector portions are disconnected and instead the phono cartridge (M2) is connected to the volume control via S1A. C8 is an RF bypass capacitor.

Voltage and Current

In addition to the signal path, many more items are included on the schematic diagram. One is the voltage at each pin of every tube. This information comes in handy for troubleshooting the equipment. Notice that the voltages at the various points in the filament circuit are included in the power-supply portion of the schematic. Also included here is the total current flowing through the rectifier (56 ma, for milliamperes). The power rating of the equipment (28 watts at 117 volts) is given at the line cord. The notes below and to the left of the line cord state the conditions under which the voltage measurements were taken.

Other Information on Schematics

Many other items are included in Fig. 11-1, and each is useful in analyzing circuit operation or in troubleshooting. For example, to the right of L2 is the drawing that shows the location of the terminals on the coil. These numbers are also included on the schematic symbols. The terminals on L3 and L4 are located below the drawing. Also given in Fig. 11-1 are the pin numbers of each element for each tube, and the connections to the resistance-capacitance component combination PC1.

144

Transformers and other components often have colored leads for identification. These are shown in Fig. 11-1 for audio-output transformer T1 and electrolytic filter capacitor C1.

The chart at the lower left gives the correct resistance reading, in ohms, from each tube pin to ground. Also given beside each coil on the schematic is its resistance (if over 1 ohm), since the easiest method of checking the condition of a coil is to measure its resistance.

Letter-and-number combinations A1 through A7, shown in the squares, are the alignment points for the receiver. Adjustments are made here, according to the instructions, to tune each stage to the proper frequency.

TRANSISTOR RADIOS

Like its vacuum-tube counterpart, a transistor radio can also be broken down into a group of simple circuits. In the transistor-radio schematic of Fig. 11-2, for example, each transistor forms a block in the operation of the over-all unit.

The signal from the station is first received at antenna coil L1. The converter transistor (Q1) performs the same function as its vacuum-tube counterpart. L2 is the oscillator coil. The signals from the oscillator and antenna are mixed in this stage, and the IF (difference frequency) is coupled to the next stage via transformer L3. The signal enters transistor Q2 at the base (B), and the amplified signal appears at the collector (C) and across the primary of transformer L4. It is then coupled to the base of transistor Q3 (another IF amplifier) via C8. The further amplified signal appears across the primary of L5. Crystal diode X2, connected to the secondary of L5, is the detector; it demodulates the IF signal, leaving the audio component at the variable arm of volume control R1. (This audio component corresponds to the original sound at the station.)

From the volume control, the audio signal goes to the base of audio-amplifier transistor Q4, where it is amplified. It is then coupled directly to the base of transistor Q5. Here the signal is amplified and coupled via transformer T1 to the speaker (SP1).

The transistor receiver in Fig. 11-2 is designed to operate directly off the 117-volt power line. Here semiconductor rectifier X1 is used in place of the tube in Fig. 11-1. Otherwise, the circuit operation is very similar to that described previously.

145

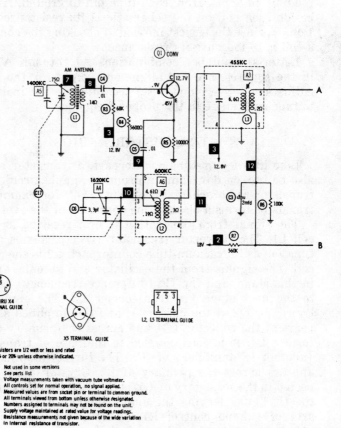

Q1 CONV

455KC

AM ANTENNA

1400KC

A5 · 7

8 · C4 · .01

C · 12.7V

B · 12.7V

A3

.9V

.45V

E

6.6Ω

L1

R3 · 68K

.75Ω

.14Ω

5

L3

2Ω

R4 · 5600Ω

3

12.8V

C5 · .01

9

R5 · 1000Ω

3

12.8V

12

A

1620KC

A4 · 10

600KC

A6 · 4.61Ω

11

C3 · 2mfd

R6 · 100K

C6 · 3.3pf

.19Ω

1.3Ω

L2

2 · R7

18V · 560K

B

B
E C

X1 THRU X4
TERMINAL GUIDE

B

E C

X5 TERMINAL GUIDE

2 5 3

1 4

L2, L5 TERMINAL GUIDE

Resistors are 1/2 watt or less and rated
10% or 20% unless otherwise indicated.

✱ Not used in some versions
⊖ See parts list
1. Voltage measurements taken with vacuum tube voltmeter.
2. All controls set for normal operation, no signal applied.
3. Measured values are from socket pin or terminal to common ground.
4. All terminals viewed from bottom unless otherwise designated.
5. Numbers assigned to terminals may not be found on the unit.
6. Supply voltage maintained at rated value for voltage readings.
7. Resistance measurements not given because of the wide variation
   in internal resistance of transistor.

Fig. 11-2. A tran-

146

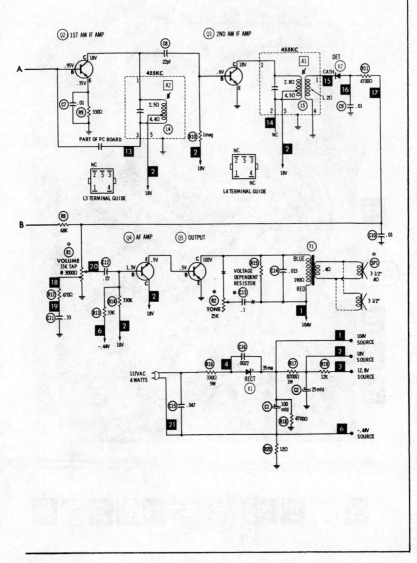

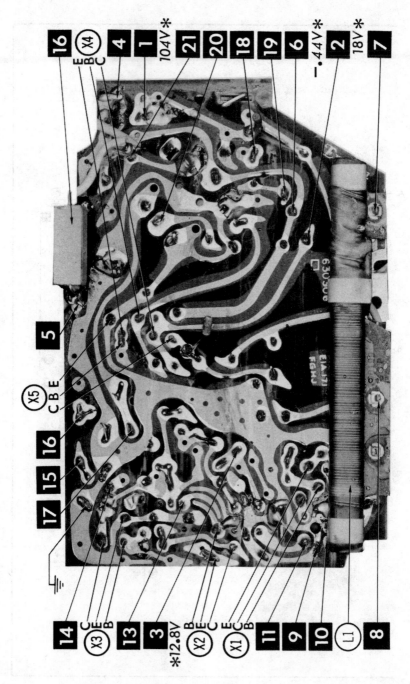

Fig. 11-3. Printed circuit used in the radio in Fig. 11-3.

The numbers 1 through 21 in the black boxes appear on the schematic and also in Fig. 11-3, a photograph of the chassis. Called CIRCUITRACE (a tradename of Howard W. Sams & Co., Inc.) this system greatly aids in locating the various points on a printed-circuit board. By referring to the schematic and Fig. 11-3 simultaneously, technicians are saved tedious tracing of the printed wiring.

FROM SCHEMATIC TO CHASSIS

One of the most difficult problems a beginner faces is to locate, on the chassis, a component included in a schematic; or to look at a schematic and construct the circuit. Unfortunately, as you saw in Chapter 1, the actual chassis does not look like the schematic. In fact, in the schematic a resistor may be shown next to a tube element, but may be at the other side of the chassis. The reason is that a schematic can show electrical connections only, but a component must also have some means of mechanical support.

Terminal strips are often included on the chassis, and the terminals utilized for connecting between two points. Not all pins are used for internal connections on all tubes, but the tube socket will have terminals for each pin. For example, for mechanical support, one end of the resistor may be connected to an unused tube-socket terminal, which is then connected by a wire at the other end of the circuit.

If you have a photograph or pictorial drawing like the ones shown in Chapter 1, a component is easy to locate. But the component can still be located, even if only the schematic is available. Just look for a familiar nearby point in the circuit. (Tube pins are usually the most convenient points.) Then see what components are connected between this point and the desired component. Next find this point on the schematic, and follow any wire connected to it. Be sure to trace out all leads connected to any tie points (terminal strips or unused tube pins). If you encounter a component not connected between the wanted one and the starting point, go back and try a different route. While such hit-and-miss tracing sounds tedious, with a little practice it soon becomes easy and fast. Remember: the fact that a component is connected to a tube-socket terminal doesn't mean there is an internal connection to the tube. This connection may be there for mechanical support only.

OTHER TYPES OF EQUIPMENT

No matter how complex, the schematic of any piece of electronic equipment can be broken down into individual stages, as you did in this chapter. Then by following the connections between stages you will be able to fit the blocks together and in this way determine the over-all operation of the circuit.

QUESTIONS

1. Where is the input normally located on a schematic?
2. What three functions are performed by the converter stage?
3. What additional aid in locating transformer leads is often included on a schematic?
4. What is the purpose of the AVC voltage?
5. How does the IF signal differ from the signal received from the station?
6. What is the best way to analyze a schematic?
7. What type of signal appears across the volume control?
8. What is the disadvantage of connecting all tube filaments in series?
9. Does an earphone or a speaker require more power for operation?
10. What is the purpose of an RF bypass capacitor?

APPENDIX A

House Wiring Symbols

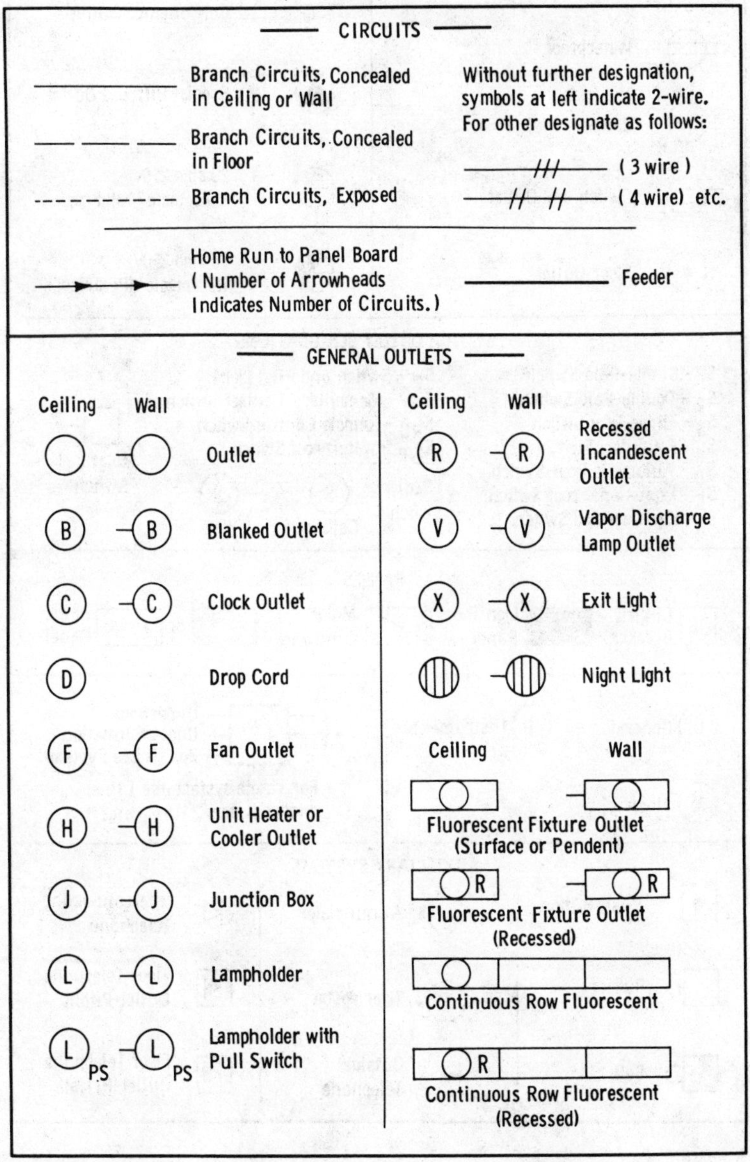

CIRCUITS

Branch Circuits, Concealed in Ceiling or Wall

Branch Circuits, Concealed in Floor

Branch Circuits, Exposed

Home Run to Panel Board (Number of Arrowheads Indicates Number of Circuits.)

Without further designation, symbols at left indicate 2-wire. For other designate as follows:

/// (3 wire)

// // (4 wire) etc.

Feeder

GENERAL OUTLETS

Ceiling	Wall	
◯	─◯	Outlet
Ⓑ	─Ⓑ	Blanked Outlet
Ⓒ	─Ⓒ	Clock Outlet
Ⓓ		Drop Cord
Ⓕ	─Ⓕ	Fan Outlet
Ⓗ	─Ⓗ	Unit Heater or Cooler Outlet
Ⓙ	─Ⓙ	Junction Box
Ⓛ	─Ⓛ	Lampholder
ⓁPS	─ⓁPS	Lampholder with Pull Switch

Ceiling	Wall	
Ⓡ	─Ⓡ	Recessed Incandescent Outlet
Ⓥ	─Ⓥ	Vapor Discharge Lamp Outlet
Ⓧ	─Ⓧ	Exit Light
◍	─◍	Night Light

Ceiling / Wall

Fluorescent Fixture Outlet (Surface or Pendent)

Fluorescent Fixture Outlet (Recessed)

Continuous Row Fluorescent

Continuous Row Fluorescent (Recessed)

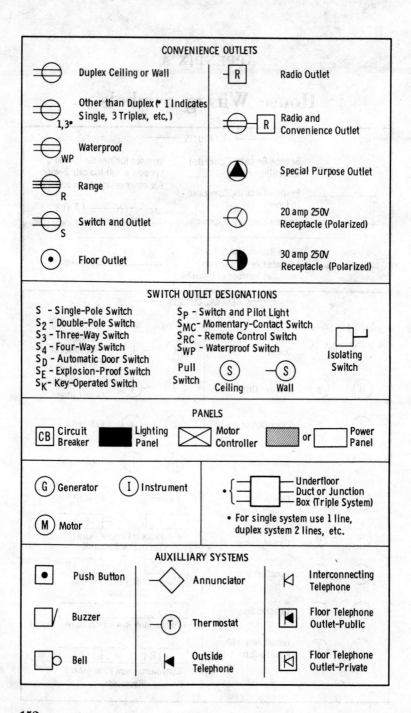

CONVENIENCE OUTLETS

Duplex Ceiling or Wall		R	Radio Outlet
Other than Duplex (* 1 Indicates Single, 3 Triplex, etc.) 1,3*		R	Radio and Convenience Outlet
Waterproof WP			Special Purpose Outlet
Range R			20 amp 250V Receptacle (Polarized)
Switch and Outlet S			30 amp 250V Receptacle (Polarized)
Floor Outlet			

SWITCH OUTLET DESIGNATIONS

S - Single-Pole Switch
S₂ - Double-Pole Switch
S₃ - Three-Way Switch
S₄ - Four-Way Switch
S_D - Automatic Door Switch
S_E - Explosion-Proof Switch
S_K - Key-Operated Switch

S_P - Switch and Pilot Light
S_MC - Momentary-Contact Switch
S_RC - Remote Control Switch
S_WP - Waterproof Switch

Pull Switch

S Ceiling   S Wall

Isolating Switch

PANELS

CB Circuit Breaker   Lighting Panel   Motor Controller   or   Power Panel

G Generator   I Instrument

M Motor

Underfloor
Duct or Junction
Box (Triple System)

* For single system use 1 line,
duplex system 2 lines, etc.

AUXILLIARY SYSTEMS

Push Button		Annunciator		Interconnecting Telephone	
Buzzer		Thermostat T		Floor Telephone Outlet-Public	
Bell		Outside Telephone		Floor Telephone Outlet-Private	

Answers to Questions

Chapter 1

1. A drawing, using symbols to represent the various parts, which shows the electrical connections of all components in a circuit. In addition, the value of components, color of leads, tube pin connections, voltage and resistance measurements, and many other items are usually included.
2. By a code letter and number.
3. It shows the various stages in the unit, and how they fit together.
4. The physical location of the components.
5. It shows each part as it actually looks in the chassis and is less expensive to produce.
6. They are the quickest, easiest, and most meaningful method of conveying the electrical connections within a circuit.
7. By an "exploded" view, which shows all the parts in their relative position, yet spreads them out so you can see each individual part.
8. The physical location of tubes and major components on top of the chassis. Certain items below the chassis may also be indicated by dashed lines.
9. Dial-cord strings, exploded views of record changers and tape recorders, motor-driven systems, and mechanical actions in organs or similar units.
10. The schematic.

Chapter 2

1. Ohm.
2. (A) To limit current (flow of electrons) in a circuit.
   (B) To provide a voltage drop.
3. An opposition to the flow of electrons through a circuit. The electrical equivalent of friction.
4. Omega (Ω).
5. A variable resistor.
6. R.
7. 27,000 ohms.
8. One whose resistance decreases when its temperature is increased.

9.

10.

Chapter 3

1. To store electrons.
2. No, they only appear to.
3. The farad.
4. The dielectric.
5. No.
6. Filter capacitors in power supplies.

7. One millionth.
8. The rotor.
9. C
10. (A) Polarized electrolytic capacitor. (B) Trimmer capacitor. (C) Nonpolarized electrolytic.

Chapter 4

1. Inductance.
2. Henry.
3. None, except for the slight amount of resistance it offers to the flow.
4. The magnetic lines of force set up by the primary cut the secondary winding.
5. Two or three solid lines ($\equiv$ or $\equiv$).
6. Choke.
7. The primary.
8. A powdered-iron core.
9. T and L
10.

Chapter 5

1. To control the flow of electrons.
2. To supply or emit electrons.
3. V
4. A gas tube.
5. The television picture tube.
6. The plate.
7. Through pins in the tube base.
8.
9.
10.

Chapter 6

1. Germanium, silicon, selenium.

2. It is not necessary.
3. NPN and PNP.
4. Base, collector, and emitter.
5. Q, X, V, T, TR
6.
7.
8.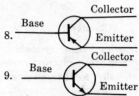
9.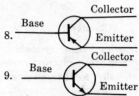
10. Voltage regulation.

Chapter 7

1. To open and close a circuit.
2. Single-pole, single-throw.
3. Single-pole, double-throw.
4. To connect one point to either of two other points.
5. An electrically operated switch.
6. The two points are mechanically (but not electrically) connected.
7. To form an electromagnet.
8. S, SW, M, E
9.
10.

Chapter 8

1. To convert an electrical signal into sound waves.
2. A fuse.
3. Incandescent and neon.
4. A cell is the basic unit; a battery is a group of cells.
5. Carbon, dynamic (or moving

coil), capacitor, ceramic, and crystal.

6.

7. ─(V)─

8. ⊥

9. ⊥╢╟╢╟⊨

10. A circuit breaker.

Chapter 9

1. It simplifies the layout of the schematic by eliminating many lines.
2. Plug section.
3. Not always, but they can be.
4. A bus line.
5. The same as for any other leads.
6. Occupy less space; less expensive in initial cost; and less expensive to assemble on chassis.
7. A shielded component.
8. That they are parts of a multiple unit.
9.

10. ▯⊏ ┥⊏ (Ⅱ)

Chapter 10

1. To convert AC to DC.
2. One to which power must be supplied.
3. No electrons will flow.
4. NPN and PNP.
5. The cathode follower.
6. From emitter to collector.
7. The cathode.
8. Common emitter, common base, and common collector.
9. Grounded cathode, grounded grid, and cathode follower.
10. The negative terminal.

Chapter 11

1. At the upper left-hand corner.
2. RF amplifier, oscillator, mixer.
3. Color of leads.
4. To automatically compensate for changes in signal strength.
5. In frequency only.
6. Break it down into individual stages.
7. Audio signal.
8. If one burns out, all tubes will go out.
9. Speaker.
10. To remove high-frequency signals present in the circuit.

Index